FROM NORTHERN IRELAND

Edited by Dave Thomas

First published in Great Britain in 2000 by
YOUNG WRITERS
Remus House,
Coltsfoot Drive,
Woodston,
Peterborough, PE2 9JX
Telephone (01733) 890066

HB ISBN 0 75431 942 3
SB ISBN 0 75431 943 1

FOREWORD

This year, the Young Writers' Future Voices competition proudly presents a showcase of the best poetic talent from over 42,000 up-and-coming writers nationwide.

Successful in continuing our aim of promoting writing and creativity in children, our regional anthologies give a vivid insight into the thoughts, emotions and experiences of today's younger generation, displaying their inventive writing in its originality.

The thought, effort, imagination and hard work put into each poem impressed us all and again the task of editing proved challenging due to the quality of entries received, but was nevertheless enjoyable. We hope you are as pleased as we are with the final selection and that you continue to enjoy *Future Voices From Northern Ireland* for many years to come.

CONTENTS

Davina Stuart	26
Adele Speer	26
Tammy Love	27
Victoria Ross	28
Lisa Hamilton	28
Joanne Moore	29
Kyle Law	29
Donna Torrens	30
Kiel Cathers	30
Kim Ross	31
Catherine Doherty	31
Lucy Sproule	32
Stacey Sproule	32
Stacey Harpur	33
Durrell Nelson	34
Ruth Montgomery	34
William Sproule	35
David Gourley	36
Natasha Logue	36
Heather Davis	37
Shalane McNeill	38
Darren Foster	38
Tracey McCaskie	39
Gillian Foster	40
Amanda Pollock	41
Caroline Graham	42
Shelley Harpur	43
Michelle Wilson	44
Malandra McNeill	44
Ian Scott	45
Judith Knox	46
Alison Williamson	47
Diana Patrick	48
Victoria Taylor	48
George Hunter	49
Ruth McMullan	50
Claire Kerrigan	50
Charlene Pak	51

Clare Harris	73
Carla Cassidy	74
Amanda Loughlin	74
Aoife McGovern	75
Brenda Rice	75
Anne McBrien	76
Claire Reilly	76
Caitlin McCann	77
Laura Hannigan	77
Tara Jayne Duffy	78
Charlene McCauley	78
Seana Higgins	79
Leanne Sweeney	79

Portadown College

Peter Strong	80

St Brigid's High School Omagh

Adelle McCarney	81
Roisin Madden	81
Melanie Warren	82
Lynn McCullagh	82
Claire Donaghy	83
Mary Nugent	83
Laura Martin	84
Eimear Teague	84
Katherine Turbett	85
Tanya McBride	86
Lisa McCallion	86
Roisin Coyle	87
Josie Devlin	87
Frances Campbell	88
Denise Bradley	89
Stephanie Duddy	90
Clodagh Hagan	90
Arlene McCollum	91
Donna Maguire	92
Danielle Moore	92

Tracy Sharkey	93
Ann Coyle	93
Joanne Campbell	94
Fionnula Haughey	94
Majella Maguire	95
Donna Treanor	95
Sinéad Monaghan	96
Kerri McCusker	96
Mairéad Gormley	97
Donna Conway	98
Clare Conlin	98
Kirsty Gormley	99
Kelly Devlin	99
Dearbhla Woods	100
Siobhan Galbraith	100
Ciara Gallagher	101
Leona O'Neill	102
Nicola Glass	102
Geraldine Nugent	103
Tanya Hughes	103
Orla Byrne	104
Marie Lynch	104
Catherine Conway	105
Kellie McKenna	106
Joanne O'Brien	106
Gemma McGlone	107
Kathryn Conwell	108
Nicola Fiddis	108
Fiona Kelly	109
Leon Murphy	110
Emma Deazley	110
Aileen Devine	111
Jade Devine	111
Chereen McGoldrick	112
Charlene Colton	112
Laura Logue	113
Hayley Early	114
Suzanne Allen	114

St Michael's Grammar School, Lurgan

The Poems

WAR?

War? War?
You mean that gory, brutal, disgusting, horrible thing?
The thing that is so murderous and hateful?
That thing which claims so many lives?

Oh no, I'm not going to be part of that!
I would be safer standing in the middle of a live volcano,
Than going to war!
I am not going to kill loads of people, or kill myself.

What? A good opportunity?
If that's what you call a good opportunity,
Goodbye, it was nice knowing you!
That's not what I call a good opportunity.
That's what I call, 'Hi God, see you in a minute!'

Would you like to go round on one leg for the rest of your life?
I know I wouldn't.
And I don't fancy using my only foot to write with either.
And on top of that,
Do you know what it smells like in a room full of soldiers?

You'll be there?
Well I must say, that's very reassuring.
I'm very glad you're willing to jump up and catch the bomb
Before it comes near me,
And stop the bullet before it cracks through my heart so quickly,
I can't see it coming out the other side.

No! I'm not going to war, never, ever, ever.
I'm not going anywhere near that terrific display of hooliganism.
I'm just going to stay here in this comfortable chair,
And if the war comes here, at least I'll die comfortably!

Jennifer Fegan (12)
Assumption Grammar School

WAR!

'Be brutal, be cold,' shouted the officer.
'Strike horror into your enemies' hearts.'
'Yes Sir!' we replied.
Although I answered, I never really understood
how to be brutal or strike horror.
I never knew why either.
'Move out and hold your rifles with pride!' roared the officer.
I felt sick when I smelt the acrid burning.
I could almost hear pain herself screaming at me.
I have never felt selfish or sordid before,
but now she grabbed and squeezed my stomach.
Guilt choked in my throat and stung my eyes.
I had seen so much death and sadness. I lost all will.
My emotion took over, I had to cry.
I had no idea of the effects of war.
In sympathy for myself but mainly others.
I couldn't kill another.
So I lifted Sara, stroked her sleek black barrel
and ended my pain.

Toni McCrissican (13)
Assumption Grammar School

WAR

War is not a pretty sight,
With blood and death around the place.
When war is around, everything is dangerous.
War is muddy, trenches are deep.
War spreads like a disease.

War is bloodthirsty and bad.
What's the point of bombing places, moving in armies
And their equipment, like tanks?
It's only going to make things worse.
War spreads like a rash.

Warheads, warfare and radiation,
What's the meaning of these words?
All I know is that they sound horrible.
Why is it that innocent people get hurt,
Are killed and get diseases,
When it might be the government's fault?
If a war ever starts over here,
I will be getting the first plane out of here.

And what's the point of war?

Tara O'Hare (12)
Assumption Grammar School

WAR

W hy does it have to happen?
A ssassinations taking place day by day.
R efugees flee their homes and countries.

I believe in world peace
S o why can't everyone else?

D isease is spread because of war.
E nemies of the world.
V ast amounts of people wiped out.
A ttacks on innocent people.
S helters are no use.
T o what length will the killers go?
A crid smells of burning flesh fill the air.
T ortured bodies piled up high.
I solation from family and friends.
N ightmares disturbing children's sleep for years.
G rief will never end.

Mary McCartan (12)
Assumption Grammar School

DEVASTATION

Bombs are exploding near and far,
Aeroplanes are circling overhead,
It'll end in a never-ending scar,
Children hold these memories in their head.

Countries destroyed, people dead,
Death has hung around like mist,
Are these soldiers right in the head?
It's a never-ending list!

Will there be an end to this pain?
The hurt goes on and on.
All our lives are going down the drain,
All those innocent people gone!

The smell of decay is all around,
More nuclear bombs are made,
Burning bodies on the ground,
How many times will there be an air raid?

Kerri Clarke (12)
Assumption Grammar School

WAR

Why do we have war?
It only causes pain.
What does it achieve?
I ask again.

As I sit here in my camp
I hear the cries of wounded men.
And what does this achieve?
I ask again.

Why didn't our leaders say 'Yes, OK'?
Instead I'm sitting here today.
And what does this achieve?
I ask myself again on this bloody day.

Aoife Stranney (12)
Assumption Grammar School

Just To Let You Know . . .

Just to let you know . . . I love you
I thank you for everything
For my clothes, for my books
And most especially for the love you have given me.

Just to let you know . . . I need you
To make me feel safe if I'm scared
To keep my spirits up if I'm sick,
To reassure me when things go wrong.

Just to let you know . . . I appreciate you
When I come home feeling tired from school
You always have a minute to spare.
Thank you for all this care.

Just to let you know . . . I'm sorry,
Sorry for talking too much
Or annoying you,
Or for not doing my chores . . . the list goes on.

Just to let you know . . . if *you* ever need *me*,
I'll always be there.

Niamh Looby (12)
Assumption Grammar School

O Praise the Lord

O praise the Lord
Our children grow
For all the extra
Things they know.

They walk and run
No longer creep
At last we get
A full night's sleep.

They fly like birds
Soar on the wing
They shout aloud
They dance and sing.

O praise the Lord
A little more
That two and two
At least make four.

They write a poem
Story or letter
And do them all
A little better.

O praise the Lord
My child has grown
My lovely child
My heart, my own.

Shauneen Fitzpatrick (12)
Assumption Grammar School

THE WAR

I hate the war,
People dropping dead in front of me.
All the bombing and hatred,
People being separated from loved ones.

All the violence and horror would make me sick,
Army troops and tanks are everywhere,
Shooting everything in their way.

Terrified people running everywhere,
Smoke and fires,
Anguish and hatred,
Grief and sadness.

Army aeroplanes flying above,
Dropping bombs on people below.
Limbs are all over the place,
But what is worst of all, dead children too.

If it isn't soldiers themselves killing people,
It is fumes from the bombs soldiers drop.
It's pure torture for anyone who has experienced this brutality,
The carnage of innocent people.

Hannah O'Boyle (12)
Assumption Grammar School

WAR

I am sitting in my tent
We had a hard day today
Several soldiers have been killed
It's carnage, I have to think, when will it be me?

I have a feeling
There is an attack coming
I can hear something . . .
Oh, it's only Smithy.

I wrote a letter to Kate today
John has started school
And little Sam is coming soon
I wish I was there.

I am feeling restless
I feel that someone is watching me
I don't want to die and leave Kate.

I thought I just heard something
But it's just Smithy, I think
Was it? What was that?
Oh no! Ahhhhh!

Laura Reid (12)
Assumption Grammar School

WAR!

Do you ever stop and think, of all
the people who died in the war?
What happened?
          How it started? Why?

Also, if all the people who were killed,
were trying to fight for their countries?
All the men, women, children and even little babies
who did not survive? Of all the horrific dangers
that they put themselves through? Why?

Because it never even crossed my mind until now!
Why do young people like ourselves,
not even think about it?
Because it was in the past, that's why!

Think of how they were killed, why they were killed.
Of all those little babies who only got crumbs, if lucky.
Why was this the way they had to live?
Oh why? It wasn't fair!

I can't stop and think
of what those poor people went through!
You know we might think we are badly off,
but just remember, never as bad as them!

Áine McClean (12)
Assumption Grammar School

WAR!

It was brutal
There was blood,
There were people crying,
Their children were dying.

It was horrendous,
I had to leave home,
I lost my dad on our travel,
I wish it was a dream I could unravel.

I could hear the gunshots,
A frightening sharp bang,
I could hear the knives slash,
People falling with a loud bash.

Why is this happening?
Will it ever stop?
This war is really vain,
These people must be insane.

I am staying in a refugee camp,
Will I ever make it home?
For this my imagination still flows,
Will I? Nobody knows, nobody knows.

Christine Deegan (12)
Assumption Grammar School

THE UNENDING WAR

Isolated in a shelter
No noise, no sound
All alone
Your parents dead.

Bang, bang, bang
Is all that's heard
Gas is in the air
Fear and panic everywhere.

People waiting to die
Soldiers waiting to attack
Not knowing what to do
Or where to go.

Is your brother alive or dead?
Will you last to the end?
Why all this pain?
Surely it is over soon.

Blood lying everywhere
What brutal people
Why? Why? Why?

Colleen McIlroy (13)
Assumption Grammar School

WAR!

Why did this war have to start?
It's not fair.
We are suffering, with
hardly any food or water
And the smell of dead bodies,
would drive anyone insane!

Being stuck in these smelly,
old bunkers is horrible.
We have been here for the past
two weeks
And all of our clothes are dirty.

All you can hear are bombs
going off, all over the city.
And you can smell the smoke
of the fires that have been
started.
It's *dreadful!*

Lots and lots of innocent
people have died
Because of the Russians.
I don't know why war
has to break out!
Why?

Gráinne McCann (13)
Assumption Grammar School

WAR IS . . .

Panic, destruction, horror
and bombs.
A madness for power by
terror and guns.

A convoy of tanks ready
to convulse,
With shiploads of ammo all
primed to destruct.

Supplies at the ready for
refugee camps,
Tear-stained faces for the
bereaved and the shocked.
Anger, pain and terror all
interlocked.

Orphans and widows with
bloodstained clothes,
Prepare many graves for all
of those who fought so bravely
for what they believed, and
now lie dead with nothing
achieved.

Karina Smyth (13)
Assumption Grammar School

WAR

War - the word sends a shiver
up my spine
Watching young
and innocent people dying.

People's lives once
full of laughter
Now shattered with
grief and pain.

Walking through
the isolated streets
I hear the cries
of the homeless.

Homeless who once
lead a perfect life
Now torn away by
this thing called war.

Buildings that once
stood towering high
Now lie crumbled
on the ground.

This war should
end.
Before the world
is full of nothing but sorrow.

Emma McKinney (13)
Assumption Grammar School

WHY WAR?

Why do people think they're always right?
Why do they fight because they think they're right?
Why do they make people suffer with pain
And fill children's dreams with terror and fright?
If I heard pain scream in the black of night,
I would blame all the people that said they were right.
If any of my loved ones went from my sight
And only appeared in my dreams at night,
I would blame the people who said they were right.

Why do people fight and kill and brutally murder on a field?
Could you lie down and dream after a fight?
Why do people kill and fight just because
There is one small chance that their opinion might be right?
How do they sleep at night?

Sara Murphy (12)
Assumption Grammar School

SCHOOL CANTEENS

If it's a bad day in the canteen the food is rotten and mouldy,
but if it is a good day there are delicious apples
and fresh sandwiches with cool orange juice.
Sometimes people can be clumsy,
drop their dinner and make a mess,
then people walk into it and slip and hurt themselves.
But anyway, it's the same old day in the canteen.
The waiting line is always very long,
people pushing and not being patient.
At the end of the school day the canteen is quiet
and has a rest for the next *canteen* school day!

Stephanie Gidney (12)
Castlederg High School

TARA

Tara is my puppy,
she's brown, black and white.
She's cute and fluffy,
funny in every way she can be.
She's a football fanatic,
in her own special way.
She's a greedy girl,
and a playful chum.
She nods her head,
she wags her tail.
Her ears hanging down,
she plays with her toys.
Delighted as she squeezes her ball,
Jumping for joy!
She's sleepy,
Nap time now, bye bye.

Shirley Moore (11)
Castlederg High School

AUTUMN

The leaves are changing colour,
The air is getting colder,
The birds are leaving,
The foxes are looking for holes,
The leaves are twirling and twisting,
The golden yellow sunset spreads across the sky,
Leaves are crunching at my feet,
Acorns and conkers are scattered on the ground.

Stuart Lecky (11)
Castlederg High School

RAINFOREST

Rainforests grow where there's lots of rain,
most of the trees there are evergreen.
There they grow for the whole year round,
in the lovely warm cosy atmosphere.
The birds in the trees and the gorillas on the ground,
Love it so much, they've come to stay.

Rainforests are homes to many animals,
like the tiger and other big cats.
The birds and the monkeys live up in the trees,
where the frogs and the ants live down on the ground.
The sounds of a rainforest makes a joyful sound,
so we want the animals to live in peace.

But some people think that this spoils the land,
so they take a digger and knock them down.
But even though the trees are planted again,
The forest never gets its original wildlife back.
The forests are cut to make way for farming,
so some beautiful birds are never seen again.

People talk about the greenhouse effect,
Oh what does it mean?
Carbon dioxide and other greenhouse gases,
contribute to climate change.
Trees use up carbon dioxide.

So let's take action! Keep our rainforests!
Help the environment, it will benefit us all.

Louise Marshall (12)
Castlederg High School

AUTUMN LEAVES

Autumn leaves come falling,
Yellow, red and brown,
I am cosy in my house,
With family all around.

Autumn leaves come falling,
All will soon be down,
The nights are getting shorter,
And Jack Frost can be found.

Autumn leaves come falling,
Floating to the ground,
Fruit is ready to be picked,
And packed off to town.

Steven Taylor (11)
Castlederg High School

THE KITTEN DISASTER

My cat Cuddles had kittens.
They started to run about.
One day my mum nearly stepped on one, she did give a shout!

The next day I went out to feed the kittens,
But the black one wasn't there.
I told my mum. She did have a scare!

We found the kitten
Under the car,
Mum said it wouldn't have gone far!

Jacqui Crowe (11)
Castlederg High School

HALLOWE'EN

At Hallowe'en we dress up as bloodsucking vampires,
Warty witches, hideous monsters and ghosts.
We scare people witless and send shivers up
their spines.

We go out and trick or treat for all sorts of
goodies, like sweets, peanuts or toffee apples.
Sometimes we would entertain families for
our treats.

Fireworks are a part of Hallowe'en.
You can get all sorts, like bangers, Catherine wheels,
air bombs and Roman candles.
Villages hold bonfires. People collect wood and
cardboard boxes.

At home we duck for apples. I collect sweets from
everyone and then I eat them in bed on
Hallowe'en night.

My cousins scoop the insides out of a turnip
and put a candle in the bottom
to make it like a
witch's lantern.

Hallowe'en is a time for enjoyment and happiness
in our lives and all over the world.

Catherine Canders (11)
Castlederg High School

THE VIKINGS

When the Vikings came to our great land,
They held a sword and a shield in each hand.
With furry big boots and furry big hats.

They came to take our wealthy loot,
Myself and my army, we decided to stand,
To give them a fight on their hands.
The battle started in early days,
We kicked in a savage way,
The swords did swish and the arrows did fly.

Blood was spilled among roars and cries,
Finally when the battle had ended,
Myself and my army were quite contented.
The Vikings left with nothing and knew what would happen if
They ever came back.

So roses are red,
But the Vikings are blue,
The Saxons are happy,
Since Alfred beat you.

Darren Love (11)
Castlederg High School

A FARMER'S LIFE

The countryside is a quiet place,
Ever so green at times.
The farmers are out working so hard,
Whilst the sheep graze in the fields.

When spring is here, farmers are growing their crops,
The lambs are born day and night.
A few days later they're skipping through the grass,
Spring is nearly over, summer is on its way.

The summer is here, the farmers begin to cut,
They cut the grass for hay.
Wrap bales soon for the cows,
Lambs are ready for the mart.

It's harvest time, the farmers go again,
The corn and wheat is gathered in.
Now it's winter, the farmers store up,
Sheep and cows have enough now through winter.

Alan Davis (12)
Castlederg High School

MY GRANNY

My granny was the best
She was always on my mind
I thought she was better than the rest
She was so very kind.

I would visit her each day before her legs were amputated.
She would help me with my homework
She made me feel that I was the only one she loved.

When she was ninety her legs were amputated.
She looked so helpless as she sat in her wheelchair.
Now that she is forever gone, I know I will miss her so.

She died when she was ninety-three.
It felt as if my heart had been broken in two.
I cried and cried all day long.

The funeral came. It was so sad.
My cousins were all there too.
Now I know it is for the best,
Now she is watching over me with the rest of my relatives.

Ashleigh McSorley (12)
Castlederg High School

WHEN MY CAT HAD KITTENS

My cat is very gentle and kind,
When you stroke her she starts to purr.
She likes to catch mice on the farm,
And take a big sleep cuddled up where it's warm.

She miaows at the door when she is hungry,
I give her a big plate of milk.
She drinks it all up,
And you know that's why her coat shines like silk.

We thought she was getting quite fat,
We said she might have little baby kittens.
I couldn't wait until they would be born,
I hoped it wouldn't be very long.

Finally the time arrived, April 10th '99.
I was so glad they had appeared.
They were so fluffy and cute,
The only problem was that their eyes were still shut.

All three of them grew up so quickly,
I was only allowed to keep one.
The other two went to a good home,
Now Tommy was left on his own.

Karen Elliott (12)
Castlederg High School

MY NEPHEW

My nephew is called Scott,
He likes to squeal a lot.
Even though he is only 3 months old,
He's the loudest in our household.

Scott is chubby and small,
He has no hair at all.
His eyes are blue
And his cheeks are red too.

Donna Hamilton (12)
Castlederg High School

FOUR SEASONS

Spring, summer, autumn and winter,
Are the four seasons of every year,
One hot, one cold, one mild, one freezing,
And each one has different kinds of weather.

Spring reminds me of flowers,
Birds coming back for winter has passed,
Insects and other creatures,
Coming out of their hibernation.

Summer reminds me of sun,
Bees buzzing about making a tune,
People lying sunbathing,
And children playing happily.

Autumn reminds me of leaves,
Twirling in the wind,
The sign of bad weather is showing,
And the squirrels are getting ready for
Their long winter's sleep.

Winter reminds me of snow,
Jack Frost is coming out to play,
Children having snowball fights,
And presents under the tree.

Stacey Loughlin (13)
Castlederg High School

MY LITTLE BROTHER

At times my brother can be fun,
And sometimes he can be boring.
He can sometimes be very bossy and cheeky,
But he is always OK inside.

When he is unhappy,
He gets very angry,
But when he is annoying,
He just talks and talks and talks.

He can be very kind,
And tries to help at times.
Sometimes he would get in the way,
When we are at work and at play.

My brother is very bright,
Although he is only eight.
He likes to think he is just great
When we have friends around.

Judith Pollock (11)
Castlederg High School

SPURS

Spurs are good,
Spurs are cool,
Spurs are the best team in the world.

David Ginola is the best,
Iverson will put you to a test.
Ian Walker will make a dive,
I will support Spurs as long as I'm alive.

Dean Whittaker (11)
Castlederg High School

AUTUMN IS MY FAVOURITE TIME OF YEAR

Summer has ended,
        Autumn is dawning,
        the evidence is there,
        the leaves are falling off the trees,
        leaving them bare.

        They fly in their splendour,
        red, orange and brown,
        or just lie there patiently
        on the ground.
        (Waiting for the wind to
        carry them away.)

        The evenings are getting darker,
        and cooler too,
        which is probably why
        everyone's catching the flu!
        Atishoo! Bless you!

        The farmers are gathering
        the harvest crops,
        and people are buying
        turkey from the shops.

        The snow will soon fall,
        Christmas is near,
        kids like it best because
        they get Christmas presents,
        but . . .
        autumn is *my* favourite time of year!

Holly Buchanan (11)
Castlederg High School

MY GRANNY

She is very tall,
But is not small,
She may be fat,
But she doesn't mind that.

My gran has grey hair,
She takes great care,
Her eyes are green,
And she is never mean.

She lives on her own,
And could sometimes moan,
I would help her tidy and clean,
But when she is working she is never seen.

She is old,
And she could sometimes scold,
But I am the greatest fan,
Of my gran.

I think she is the best gran
In the whole wide world.

Davina Stuart (11)
Castlederg High School

PEOPLE

Some people are big,
Some people are small,
Some people are fat,
Some people are tall,
Everyone is different in their own little way,
And everyone changes every day.

Boys, girls, dark and fair,
Women, men, long and short hair,
Young and old, fit and stiff,
Black and white, happy and sad,
And everyone changes every day.

Adele Speer (12)
Castlederg High School

IN AUTUMN

In autumn when the
tree leaves fall,
They lie against
my garden wall.
And in the morning
I rise,
I see the birds,
to my surprise.
They duck and dive,
and look for seed,
Unaware that pussy
is waiting with a hungry greed.
She sits upon the wall
so high,
And watches the birds
who do not fly.
So when I rise
and open the door,
The cat is gone
and the birds are no more.

Tammy Love (12)
Castlederg High School

My Wishes

I wish I had a brown and white horse,
Just like the one my granny has.
It runs about the fields all day,
And at night stays in the stable bedded with hay.

Her name is Bessie,
My granny called her Bessie after Bessie Bell Mountain
as she is so high and beautiful.
When she sees me coming,
Bessie knows it's time for grooming.

Bessie is so good and quiet,
She stands very still while you groom her.
When it's time to go home,
I give out a moan!

Victoria Ross (11)
Castlederg High School

My Little Sister

My little sister is so sweet
She sings in her bed and falls fast asleep.
When morning comes
She sucks her thumb.
Throughout the day she likes to play,
With anything she finds in her way.
At meal times she's so good,
She eats every morsel of food.
Then she gets tired and goes to bed,
Finally she lays down her sleepy little head.

Lisa Hamilton (12)
Castlederg High School

OMAGH

One Saturday afternoon at 10 past 3,
a bomb exploded which affected you and me.
Only 13 miles away people were dying,
mothers were screaming, children were crying.
I sat in the chair waiting for news,
already a family's light had been fused.
Some terrorist group called *The Real IRA*,
had brought loss to a family on that very day.
Two unborn twins and twenty-nine others lost their lives,
because of sick animals with bombs, guns and knives.
The town of Omagh is now partly destroyed,
a town which was treasured and always enjoyed.
Mothers, fathers, sisters and brothers were lost,
nobody now can replace the cost.

Joanne Moore (12)
Castlederg High School

ONE HALLOWE'EN NIGHT

One Hallowe'en night
I got a great fright
From a man with a mask and a bright light
He wanted to fight
I said 'All right'
I ran so fast he couldn't see me in sight
The man came after me
He said 'You'll see'
When the man started to run he got stung by a bee
He said 'Come back here or you'll see
I'll come after you with this giant bee'
I ran and ran till I got home
And my mum sprayed me with foam.

Kyle Law (13)
Castlederg High School

MR NOBODY

Do you know this funny little man
As silent as a mouse
Who does the mischief that is done
In everybody's house?
There's no one ever sees his face
But we must all agree
That every cup we break was cracked
By this funny little man.
It's him who always tears our books
And leaves the door ajar,
It's he that takes our pencils
And scatters them afar.
The drinks we never spill
The shoes and coats that lie around
They're not *ours* you see
They belong to this funny little man
            Mr Nobody!

Donna Torrens (12)
Castlederg High School

THE PUNY GUY

There was once a puny guy
And his name was Bill,
His legs were skinny, his voice was shrill.
He once tried weightlifting,
And he worked on his thighs,
But now all they say is
'Who ate all the pies?'

Kiel Cathers (13)
Castlederg High School

SUMMER DAY

On a summer's day, sitting by the river
Watching the sun go down,
I sit there and gaze at the water
As it flows like silk over the rocks.

As the evening passed something caught my eye,
It glinted and shone like a bright light,
It was a beautiful rainbow trout feeding on flies
Which was sitting peacefully enjoying the afternoon sun.

As I thought, I thought about myself,
My belly grumbled,
I decided to go for my dinner, so,
I'm off.

Kim Ross (13)
Castlederg High School

HOMEWORK

Homework is such a bore
It's just like doing a chore
When you're at school it's work, work, work
When you're at home it's the same
At the end of each class the teacher tells us our homework
It doesn't matter how long you spend on it
You seem to get something wrong anyway
Almost every day now we have homework
If it's not maths, science, history or geography
It's the worst subject of all - English
Each day it's like a routine
Going home and doing your homework.

Catherine Doherty (13)
Castlederg High School

PARENTS

She shouts and nags every single second of every single day,
But I scream and tell her it's all right.
So she suggests getting someone into help tidy the stuff away,
So I say yes that would be fine, but she has already changed her mind
And I have to tidy it myself - as if!

Mum never nags at all, just about my room,
So I'll tell her it's clean so I can rest for the day without the nagging,
But she'll walk in and it's as messy as it's ever been.

But eventually I tidy it,
As I'm sick of hearing about the mess
And when it's all done Mum looks pleased
And I can have a little rest.

Lucy Sproule (14)
Castlederg High School

ALIENS

Aliens are strange wee green creatures from another planet,
Aliens are well known for their little UFOs.

Which land on Earth and abduct Earthling creatures like myself,
It seems to be that they like people with freckles and long, curly hair.

Thank goodness I don't have long curly hair.
I spend loads of money on products that keep my hair straight,
Like straighteners out of Boots,
The choice for you.

But the Earthlings are far too big to get in the UFO,
So aliens flush us down the toilet.
But, for some strange reason, we end up on their planet anyway.

Stacey Sproule (12)
Castlederg High School

THE LAMPING LURCHER

When the moon has gone
And the nights are dark
With a dog in the car
We leave the park.

Destination unknown
Dad shines around
Then we reach some fields
Where rabbits abound.

Dad then gets Bonnie
She's put on the slip
And off runs a rabbit
With a hop and a skip.

They twist and turn
With the speed of light
Then Bonnie strikes
That's the first of the night!

We walked in the darkness
For an hour or so
Eighteen rabbits in all -
It was now time to go.

Now the foxes round here
Have been causing some bother
The farmer lost lambs
To one fox or another.

We'll be back here again
With this lurcher and light
To sort out these foxes
And end farmers' plight.

Stacey Harpur (12)
Castlederg High School

MILLENNIUM

The year 2000 is drawing near,
Time to reach the millennium year.
Out off the 20th century we have gone,
Into the 21st with a bomb!
Parties go on day and night,
Will not stop to morning light.
People cannot believe it's here,
So much has happened in a thousand years.
Generations have come and gone,
Still the memories will live on.
In the children's eyes you'll see,
Happy faces filled with glee.
So now the big day has come and gone,
We must step forward and move on.

Darrell Nelson (13)
Castlederg High School

THE ENVIRONMENT

People rip our world apart,
Without a second thought,
For silly things like wooden chairs
And paper on our walls.

Fumes of petrol fill the air,
That our lungs breathe in.
As they break our ozone layer,
The global warming then begins.

They make GM foods for us to eat,
Perhaps it seems a treat,
But these juicy fruits we eat,
Hold a deep, dark secret.

Look at our world today,
So beautiful and bright,
What will the future hold,
If we don't stop today.

Ruth Montgomery (13)
Castlederg High School

OUR GERMAN SHEPHERD

A German Shepherd pup was on our mind,
We looked in the Telegraph to see what we could find.
A breeder from Glenarm had ten pups to show,
So we mounted the jeep and away we did go.

After two hours we went right to the farm,
A big dog on guard but we came to no harm.
Five boys and five girls, we were spoilt for choice,
A lot of barking just to prove they had a voice.

We chose a wee fluffy lassie, bright and bold,
We wrapped her in a blanket to keep out the cold.
When we got her home we could not settle on a name,
Tara and Lucy, they all sounded much the same.

At last we agreed because time was going by,
We called her Diamond for the sparkle in her eye.
Three week later, she's got a much stronger bark
And she makes me more secure, especially after dark.

William Sproule (11)
Castlederg High School

WINTER NIGHT

One winter night the
Storms were blowing and
The clouds were
Out.
I heard the crash of
Doors so I went
Outside,
A door
Of a shed just came
Passing by and
Nearly hit me on the head.
I got all that I could and put
It against so no more
Would come
Passing by.
I got into bed and hoped
For the best that no
More doors would
Come off any sheds.

David Gourley (13)
Castlederg High School

SCHOOL

School starts at nine and ends at ten-past three,
The teachers are glad to see us go and believe me, so are we.
It hit twelve, three hours to go,
Everybody jumps and shouts
'Uhoooooo.'

Teachers, preachers of every kind,
Big ones, small ones, be quiet there's one behind!
They go on and on, they never shut up,
'Keep quiet, you rude little mutts.'

Natasha Logue (13)
Castlederg High School

AUTUMN

The leaves are falling gently
Bouncing on the windowpanes
The red, gold and crispy leaves
The trees are full of nuts and berries
And the squirrels running by.

It's time for harvest in the churches
Beautifully decorated with flowers
Nuts, fruits and vegetables all around.

And songs being sung
The sky is red
The sunlight is clear
The fields are now golden
With some frosty morning
Soon swallows will have left us
And flown overseas
And the hedgehogs are making
Their beds
Under the trees lie some
Leaves for some animals
To lie in for a bed.

Heather Davis (13)
Castlederg High School

DISCOS

On a Friday night
It's the party night
Go have a shower
Get all dressed up
Then go and have
A good night out.

I see this cute boy
Standing alone
And I ask him
'How about a dance?'

He said 'No thanks,
My wife is standing
Waiting to get some
Drinks.'

Shalane McNeill (12)
Castlederg High School

HOMEWORK

Homework, oh what a pain
Time used in vain
Maths to do, profit or loss
French to learn no time to waste.

English, the language I know best
Science must revise
For the big test
Technology pleases me.

Getting on the yellow bus
Thinking of all the homework
English - an essay
And maths a bar chart.

In the front door
School left behind
More homework to do
Oh, what a bore.

Darren Foster (14)
Castlederg High School

SCHOOL

People say
School is the best days of our lives.
Advice.
Do we really need it?

Homework
That's when the moaning starts.
Excuses
Are they telling the truth?

Friends
Some of them are a laugh.
Fighting
Why can't they just agree?

Earrings
Teachers should just let us wear them.
Rules
Why do we have to obey them?

Tracey McCaskie (12)
Castlederg High School

MY GRANNY
(This poem was inspired by old age!)

She's very good to me
Never ask any questions
When she wants a cup of tea.

It's quiet when she's not around
And noisy when she is
She's nice at heart
But mad in the head
And she's really good to me.

My granny gives me money
To buy things that I like
'Cause if I ask mummy
She'd say 'On your bike!'

I really like my granny
She's very good to me
So I never ask any questions
When there's something in it for me.

She has one favourite granddaughter
Guess who it could be?
Of course it's me!
Or could it be . . .
Oh *please* let it be me.

Gillian Foster (12)
Castlederg High School

WATCH OUT THE OLD WOMAN'S ABOUT!

The old woman who lives next door,
She wears long clothes, that are tore.
She's scary and she's rude,
But she's a real rich dude.

The old woman who lives next door,
Please stop it I can't take any more.
She's fat and has grey hair,
But she says she doesn't care.

The old woman who lives next door,
Please stop it I can't take any more.
She has a cat and a dog,
And she also has a frog.

The old woman who lives next door,
Please stop it I can't take any more.
When she goes out, she wears green,
And she's also very mean.

The old woman who lives next door,
Please stop it I can't take any more.
She never did share,
And she looks like a bear.
You've guessed it she's called *Witch-Bear.*

Amanda Pollock (13)
Castlederg High School

OLD MRS BLOSSOM

Mrs Blossom or so I've been told
Is an elderly lady
Seventy-five years old

She stays in her house
And seldom is seen
But when she is
She always wears green

She is very groovy
And likes playing records
From what I hear
Her favourite's, the Beatles

But then she started
Acting funny and strange
And people would say
That she was deranged

I looked at her closely
And she was kind, funny and gentle
But the more I thought of it
I knew she was mental

And so I phoned up the doctor and nurse
To come and take her
Before she got worse

They came the next day
And took her away
I really hope she gets better
That's all I can say.

Caroline Graham (12)
Castlederg High School

THE CHANGING ENVIRONMENT

The environment is changing,
With every passing year.
Man and machine wreak havoc,
Changing landscapes far and near.

The countryside is suffering,
We miss the robin's song,
The birds that sang amongst the trees,
Have nearly almost gone.

The rabbits way out in the fields,
Have nowhere left to hide,
We've ripped their homes out from the ground,
Where they did once abide.

The fox and badger nearly gone,
The otter from the stream,
The corncrake and the cuckoo,
Never heard or never seen.

The bluebell and the buttercup,
The wee wild primrose too,
Have gone and may never be seen again,
By the likes of me and you.

So you see, the damage has now been done,
By the men who have no sense,
I wish they'd stayed where they belonged,
On the other side of the fence.

The environment is being destroyed,
It may never be the same,
And if someone doesn't stop this now,
It will drive us all insane.

Shelley Harpur (14)
Castlederg High School

HOMEWORK!

Who needs homework?
Not me or you.
Homework is just things that
Takes up all the spare time we get.

That's it, just still boring old things,
No one needs!
Well I don't need homework,
Do you?

I hate homework,
I really do!
It's like doing a chore,
Every night till you leave school,
Homework, homework, homework!

Boring!
Come on you must agree with me,
It is stupid,
Or is it?

Michelle Wilson (13)
Castlederg High School

HOMEWORK

Homework is so boring,
You get some every day,
No time for anything you like,
Just boring homework.

Homework is so boring,
And so hard as well,
Homework keeps you back,
From things you want to do.

Homework is so boring,
I hope that you agree,
Not many people like it,
Just agree with me.

Homework is so boring,
I don't want some anymore,
I don't need homework,
What about you?

Malandra McNeill (14)
Castlederg High School

CONFLICT

Conflict can be good
Conflict can be bad
Conflict is a way of life
Conflict can be sad.

Conflict can make you rich
Conflict can make you poor
Conflict is not always the right way
Conflict can make you unsure.

Conflict can be with parents
Conflict can be with friends
Conflict is always the wrong conclusion
Conflict can be with costs.

Conflict can make you depressed
Conflict can make you cry
Conflict I know is the wrong way
Conflict can make you die.

Ian Scott (13)
Castlederg High School

SISTERS

I come through the door to the table,
I sit down and get my books out,
My sister is sitting beside me
And she's beginning to shout.

I try my best to ignore her,
When finally she begins to stop,
We are sitting in the peaceful room,
Trying to get on with our work.

She then gets up and leaves,
I now have got some peace,
I can hear the door bang behind her,
As she runs out of the house.

I'm nearly finished my French now,
And starting the rest of my work,
When suddenly I hear a shout,
And my sister is back to annoy me.

She lifts my book and throws it,
I give a loud shout,
I tell her to get out of the room,
Before I kick her out.

But then Mum arrives home,
And asks us what we are doing,
I tell her 'That slimy sister is annoying me,'
And Mum tells her to get out.

Judith Knox (13)
Castlederg High School

NEIGHBOURS

Mum comes in, she's in a bad mood,
'There are bad neighbours in our neighbourhood.
They're out there right now and annoying my head.'
That's what she came in frustrated and said.

'Move this, move that they said to me,
I'm a busy woman don't they see.
They think they will rule, run, ruin this place.'
Just calm down now.

'I can't calm down that's the thing,
They've got me in this mood,
My temper's wearing thin.
Get me a cup of tea, that's a good girl.'

The door bell rings, it's the new neighbours,
I answer the door, they scream and shout.
Mum is furious and she comes out,
They say to her 'Could you move the car?'

Mum says 'No, it's our own land,'
The man says 'We need to park our van.'
'Park it somewhere else' Mum says,
Dad comes in and she tells him what happened.

Alison Williamson (14)
Castlederg High School

THE MAN NEXT DOOR!

An old man who lived next door
Always slept on the floor.
His name was Dan,
He was a funny man.

He shouted with glee
When I sat on his knee.
And he called me Dearee
As my name was O'Leary.

He made me giggle
Until I wiggled.
When he came to our house
He thought he saw a mouse.

When he died
I cried and cried.
I miss his laugh
Does that sound daft?

Diana Patrick (12)
Castlederg High School

THE MOON

The moon is like a big potato in the sky
and little men from different
planets are often passing by.
If they're feeling hungry they
eat just a bit for dinner.
That's why the moon is sometimes fat
but at other times it's thinner.

Victoria Taylor (12)
Castlederg High School

THE NIGHT OF THE BIG MATCH

It was the night of the big match,
Everyone was tense,
Everyone was watching it,
Man Utd v Bayern Munich.

The match had begun,
The fans were all excited,
Bayern got a better start,
But Utd fought back.

Bayern scored a goal,
Utd's fans went boo!
Everything went quiet,
They were all shocked.

Bayern scored another goal,
Bayern's fans were excited,
Utd fought back,
But couldn't score.

Utd scored from a corner,
Everyone got all excited,
Utd scored another goal,
And then another goal.

The players were all excited as well as the fans,
After all of this the whistle went,
Utd were the champions of Europe,
They had done the *treble.*

George Hunter (12)
Castlederg High School

CHRISTMAS

All the children shout with joy,
Santa is coming late tonight with toys
That will give us great delight.

Under the tree is where they'll be,
Under the tree all wrapped up in paper just for me.

Can I hear the sleigh bells coming!
It's so exciting, I can't wait until morning.

I sit alone and think at night,
What will he bring me that I would like?

A cat or a dog, I would like a puppy
If I was being polite.

I really do like Christmas running down the stairs
To see all the Christmas presents and the Christmas tree.

Ruth McMullan (13)
Castlederg High School

PEOPLE

Some people are bossy,
Some people are kind,
But then there are people
who don't even have minds.

Some people are loud,
Some people are noisy,
But then there are people
who are really lousy.

Some people have big ears,
Some people have small ears,
But then there are people
who don't clean theirs for years.

Some people have blonde hair,
Some people have brown hair,
But then they are people
who have no hair.

But in some way everyone is different.

Claire Kerrigan (13)
Castlederg High School

SPACE

Space is full of mystery, but an interesting place as well.
Always full of surprises.
Oh!
Who knows what's out there?
Planets, moons or stars or maybe aliens!
Or even shooting stars.

So many stars,
Millions maybe billions or
Zillions or trillions (whatever that is!)
Stars in space have no end!
Even if you want them to.

There are lots of planets,
Maybe many more!
Some we mightn't have discovered yet!
But I'll always know,
In space there are endless planets and moons.

There never seems to be an end in *space*.

Charlene Pak (12)
Castlederg High School

MY DREAM ABOUT WRESTLING

One Friday night,
I was dressed in white.
I tuned in to Sky Sports One,
Wrestling came on.

Two big men came out,
Undertaker and Big Show
And The Rock and Stone Cold
Came on.

It was nearly over,
Five minutes to go,
But The Rock and Stone Cold
Won.

After it showed a phone number
So I phoned it,
I was on my way to America.

I woke the next morning
And I realised it was a dream.

Stuart Sproule (12)
Castlederg High School

HALLOWE'EN

Hallowe'en is a time for trick or treating,
Fireworks and sparklers too.
Bobbing for apples and eating nuts
And horrible monsters and ghouls.

At this time of year it is very scary
With bangs and booms in the sky,
With bright sparks and loud bangs
Up in the dark night.

The bonfire is lit and burning away
As light beams upon my face
The heat is nice.
I enjoy the scenery as the fireworks
Light up the sky.

Claire Smyth (12)
Castlederg High School

WRESTLING

When wrestling was on
There were two men,
Fighting with each
Other.

They hit one and
Other.
Then the man hit
The referee.

Another ref came out
And counted.
It went one, two,
By then the man got up.

The man was shocked
At him.
Then The Rock came out
And hurt one of them.

Then he did a rock
Bottom on him.
The Rock pinned him
One, two, three.

Alan Williamson (12)
Castlederg High School

THE MOON IS A LONELY PLACE

The moon is a lonely place
It's not particularly special
Not like other planets with rings or three moons
It's not even a real planet just a satellite
And for this reason and this reason only
It is treated unfairly - because it's different
Bullied because it's not the same
The moon is a lonely place
It hangs in that vast black web with no friends
Struggles to get free from the heartache and sorrow
The moon is a lonely place
The digs and dents didn't appear from nowhere
Rocks were hurled from Jupiter and such
It was painful but there was nowhere to run
And no one to turn to
So in the morning there wasn't a moon anymore
The moon was a lonely place.

Anthea Humphreys (12)
Collegiate Grammar School

WHAT IS THE SOUND OF . . . ?

What is the sound of a tree falling in the woods?
What is the sound of water rushing by in a river?
What is the sound of a raging fire burning the beautiful forest?
Can sound exist if there's no one around to hear it?
What is the sound of a dying animal?
What is the sound of a strong storm?
What is sound?
Can sound exist if there's no one around to hear it?

Danielle Graham (12)
Collegiate Grammar School

MY GRANNIE
(1924-1999)

It was like a black cloud
had passed over me
when you died
on Friday 24th.

I was with the principal
when Mum told me you
had passed away.
It was like someone
had taken a chunk
out of my life.
You were my best friend.
Mum took me to the hospital.
You looked so pale and dull,
you didn't look like Grannie.
I kept saying 'Wake up.'

The funeral was worse,
it poured out of the heavens.
Everyone was sorry
to hear what happened.
I will always remember you
as my best friend.

Gillian McFarland (12)
Collegiate Grammar School

EXAMINATION TRAUMATISATION

When our teachers give us tests from hell,
We cannot wait for the bell.
Rapidly we run for lunch
And munch and munch and munch.

When we've chewed our way through dinner,
We hope that our tests are winners.
Gulping chips and dunking curry,
Full and happy,
A class of grinners!

Once again we are back in class,
Our pens held tightly
And we knew rightly,
That we were going to pay,
Better not delay.

The hours are ticking by,
We all let out a big sigh.
What's that I hear, is it the bell?
Released at last from our prison cell!

Rachel Armstrong (12)
Collegiate Grammar School

A LION IN THE WILD

I am the king of the land,
Prowling through the night.

I have respect from all the animals,
They do what I say.

When I see my prey they run out of sight,
I run after them with my big, fat body.

I grab them with my big paws
And I eat them with my strong teeth.

I leave the rest for my cub,
We may seem wild but we care for our young.

Sara Rahma (12)
Collegiate Grammar School

RAIN

Why does badness have to come,
When goodness is all around?
Hatred follows us around
When badness batters the window
Like a roaring sea.

When the sun is out we all are happy,
No hatred follows us anymore.
No more howling sea at our ears
And no hatred to look at,
Splashing and splashing about.

I wish badness never came
And goodness was always there.
No hatred ever to darken a door
The sea is calm and blue,
I wish.

When it rains
Puddles are left,
They evaporate and go away.
Violence makes puddles,
Violence makes pain.
It doesn't go away
But a strain on life is marked forever.

Linda Wallace (12)
Collegiate Grammar School

LIFE, MEANING, DESTINY

Life, meaning, destiny,
These describe our existence.
But stop, think, wonder why,
What is the point?
Are our lives planned out for us,
Or are we just like bubbles floating around,
Waiting to pop at any given time?

I don't think I have a destiny,
I don't think I have a purpose.
My life is meaningless.
Will I be a president, a doctor or an actress,
Or will I never make a difference?
In this huge universe, I just exist.
Can I ever achieve anything,
Or will I be just like a bubble,
Popped before getting anywhere?

Gillian Beare (13)
Collegiate Grammar School

THE SNAIL

Gliding and sucking,
determined to complain.
Taking anything he can find,
as he moves along the dusty old carpet.

Leaving a line behind him,
he looks for more.
A slow mover,
hunting for prey.

Contracting and lengthening,
as he moves.
Taking his time,
as he carries everything on his back.

He moves to music in his head,
his heart beating,
as he glides along
the floor.

Tanya Dunn (13)
Collegiate Grammar School

LOOK AT ME

Look at me now,
Football supreme,
Sweet as an angel
Like strawberries and cream.

Look at me now,
Family spread around.
Auntie in Glasgow,
But this is where I'm bound.

Look at me tomorrow
What will I do?
Will I be happy,
Or withered and blue?

Look at me in the future,
In 60 or so years,
With false teeth in my mouth
And hearing aids in my ears.

Holly Brooker (12)
Collegiate Grammar School

PEACE

An air of harmony hangs around her,
Shining through the crowd,
Optimistic of the future,
She leads a happy life.

But she was not always this way,
For in her past she sees,
Death, destruction and a blackness,
That she could not control.
The person she was then,
Would rather be forgotten,
Just like life around,
Would rather forget her.

The feeling is 'Learn from experience,'
She does and enjoys life to the full,
She's worked so hard to make it that way,
And she would never go back.

Gayle Rutherford (13)
Collegiate Grammar School

I WONDER

I wonder why the grass is green
And why the wind cannot be seen?

I wonder why the clouds are white
And why my pet dog seems to bite?

I wonder why the stars must glow
And why the clouds must move and flow?

I wonder why the rain is clear
And why I have so much to fear?

I wonder how the trees grow big
And why my aunt must wear a wig?

I wonder if my mother knows
All these things I do suppose?

Samantha McMenamin (13)
Collegiate Grammar School

IMAGINE PEACE

Two different words, two separate thoughts
But why do we have to row about it?
I mean we eat the same food
We both watch TV
We both go to school
And we both have feelings
We both have a heart
Two eyes and two ears
We both have a family that care for us
We will both have a Christmas
And face the millennium together
Although here is a history
We can change the future
Friends not enemies
Happiness not sorrow

Donna Moffitt (12)
Collegiate Grammar School

AGORAPHOBIA!

A planet among planets,
A universe of stars,
An entanglement of galaxies,
Between the planet moon and Mars.

A field among fields,
A universe of seeds,
An entanglement of growth,
Between the flowers and the weeds.

A heart among hearts,
A universe of care,
Is it possible to wonder,
How I exist out there!

Naomi Beatty (13)
Collegiate Grammar School

THE CAT

Lurking quietly in the bushes,
Camouflaged and disguised,
Claws and teeth at the ready,
Balancing in a ready position,
Waiting patiently to pounce and kill.

Daring and skilful,
Stalking quietly around its prey,
Suddenly the time is right,
And it moves in for the kill,
Gracefully, accurate and fast,
Determined to be successful.

Laura Gilfillan (13)
Collegiate Grammar School

WAR

Why, rouse me when I sleep?
Why search for secrets that I keep?
Why, when all around is sound
Break me from the chains with which I am bound?

Does it pleasure you to see those tears
I cause to people when I am near?
You summon me from where I rest
And put my destruction to the test.

I know I'll be called for once again
Spreading my wickedness, the hurt and the pain,
But I ask of you now to let me be,
The only chance left for humanity.

Marnie Crawford (13)
Collegiate Grammar School

THE BULLY

He walks about with his shirt hanging out
and always gives a shout.
He shoves people out of his way
and wears a scowl all day.

He teases my best friend
and I wish that it would end.
He takes our crisps and doesn't pay
and always gets his own way.

You never dare to tell on him,
he may tear you limb for limb.
But when it comes to tests and work,
he's always guaranteed to shirk.

Lisa Carleton (12)
Collegiate Grammar School

THE WORLD THROUGH MY WINDOW

I lay on my bed
Staring out the window
At the schoolboy climbing a tree
The old lady on her rocking chair knitting
A dog sitting still yet ready to pounce
There I have seen a rocket heading off to space
A huge colourful umbrella blocking off the rain
Watching a horse jumping, gracefully and proud.

The frame of my window
Cuts everything down
Making it into a picture with a frame
As I stare at the huge pieces of cotton wool
I make these pictures
With details plain to see
But they're the perfect details
Which are only plain to me.

Julianne McNulty (13)
Collegiate Grammar School

SHOEBOXES FOR ROMANIA

We've covered the shoeboxes in pink and blue
The little Romanians, we're thinking of you
Our head teacher has told us about you.
She goes there every year
She helps the children and gives them gifts
They are all so very dear.
A toothbrush and some toothpaste
I though you would need that
I want to give and share
And show you that I really care.

Declan McClelland (13)
Lisanally Special School

FOOTBALL

Football is my favourite sport
What a thrill it gives
When the football coach comes to school
To teach us all the skills.
He shows me how to score those goals
I only see on TV.
I try hard and wonder if I'll ever be
As great as Michael Owen.
Liverpool is my favourite team,
It is the best I've ever seen.
The footballers are quick and fit,
They can score goals
        with just one kick.

Kyle Anderson (12)
Lisanally Special School

THE RIVER

Flowing freely
  Around the river bend
    Twisting playfully
      Its crystal-clear water
        Splashing against the bank
          And its visible stone at the bottom
            Is washed clean by the ice-cold water
Eveything's still except for the gentle gush
                of the water
A cool yet euphoric feeling fills the air
  Entranced by the beauty.
    The river, the perfect picture of our
            undisturbed nature

Anne Marie McGrade (13)
Mount Lourdes Grammar School

PEACE

Another murder, another war,
Is on the news today.
People fighting for no reason,
Throwing bombs and shooting away.

Why should innocent people die
For things they do not do.
Losing loved ones and family
And losing their spirit too?

There's one thing that we want,
Oh why can they not see
That all we want is peace and love
And to live in harmony?

With all their bombs and all their guns,
They think they hold the key,
To find a better world for us
Should war be our history?

If they could look through our eyes,
Would they see what I see?
Probably not. They want their war
They do not want our peace.

Charlene Curran (13)
Mount Lourdes Grammar School

DREAMS

A thing you cannot explain,
Sometimes it seems really insane,
Candyfloss slides, sunflower skies,
Some even dream of daffodil pies.

Mysterious and confusing,
Sometimes, not a bit amusing
When you're lying in your bed
These funny things pop into your head.

Jemma Logan (12)
Mount Lourdes Grammar School

HOLIDAYS

Summer holidays are the best time of year
go to a caravan park
but always make sure the seaside is near
pitch a tent
on your favourite site
right next to the spot to fly your kite.

Then when you are all done
Relax and enjoy yourself and have some fun!
Sit in your sun seat or go to the beach
and have a snack, an apple or a peach.

And last thing at night, when you are worn out
go to the pub and have a laugh or a shout
then go back
and collapse in your tent
then realise you put it up bent!

In the end you sleep on the ground
oh, such bliss, not a sound
saying thank you God for Mother Earth
after a full day's mirth.

Denise Kelly (12)
Mount Lourdes Grammar School

LOVE

It controls your head, heart and body.
The passion explodes inside us,
It take two to tango, twist and twirl
It can dine, dance, create a fuss.

The spark, the fire, the lightning.
It's the apple in their eye.
It slips into your life when least expected,
It makes you laugh, sing and cry.

It lights up your life, reflecting the sun.
Emotions begin to rise,
Sparks flying, storms raging,
It causes heartbreak, tears and lies.

It turns their hearts inside out,
Their stomachs begin to flutter.
When two soulmates intertwine,
Their hearts receive a judder.

It pulls the heartstrings to and fro.
It shouts aloud 'Support each other'
It confuses their brain and body,
And leaves them with a lover.

Carol McCusker (13)
Mount Lourdes Grammar School

THE COUNTRYSIDE

The smell of trailing honeysuckle
Fills my nose.
The crystal-blue river
Trickles down the rough grey mountain.
Woolly, cream sheep graze in the lush
green fields.

Bright blue sky,
Gentle breeze blowing,
Busy bees humming,
Masses of snowdrops, buttercups,
Primroses and bluebells
Decorate the fields.

Horses munch tender, spring grass.
Silver waterfalls splash
As they roll down the mountainside.
Pretty, colourful butterflies
Flutter over golden cornfields.

On this lovely spring morning
The countryside is heaven.

Theresa Smyth (11)
Mount Lourdes Grammar School

THE FIRE

The fire, it started life, but a flicker,
A flame and then a blaze,
Reducing to dust, the chair made of wicker,
Devouring all, in a frenzied craze.

Thriving on furniture and all in the room,
Advancing, accelerating, progressing,
As it attacked with vengeance and venom,
Thrusting forward, stealthily pressing.

The house was devoured in a haze of fumes,
As fire engines rushed to the scene.
They hosed gallons of water, at the flames, in spumes,
The house was unrecognisable from what it should have been.

The fire it roared and hissed with might,
But gradually reduced to half.
It did put up a heroic fight,
But soon it hissed its last.

Sinead McDonagh (13)
Mount Lourdes Grammar School

THE EMIGRANT

Times are hard, I cannot find work.
I'm leaving old Ireland -
I'm bound for New York.
I'm sad and lonely leaving behind
My family and friends -
A new life to find!
I wonder what lies ahead
As I board the ship
Bound for a strange country -
After a long, long trip.

I have no choice. I have to go.
I hope to find riches
And be poor no more.
The ship is now sailing -
Tears make my eyes burn.
Farewell dear Ireland!
One day I'll return!

Emma Foy (11)
Mount Lourdes Grammar School

FIRE

It yanks open the door as its rage begins to grow
Skipping past the office, surging past the lockers
The small insignificant animals begin to feel
the tremble.
It swiftly advances past the stairs as
the once sturdy building starts to fall apart.
Whirling and gliding as it performs a
graceful dance.
It manoeuvres through the dark deserted classrooms
Flicking aside the chairs and desks in its way
Meandering along the corridors, staggering on
the steps
Plodding and ploughing through the canteen
Cooking the smallest pea to a cinder
It punches down the exit only to be greeted
by its fear
And as soon as it had started, it had finished
Leaving behind the destroyed remains of a
school.

Aisling McQuaid (13)
Mount Lourdes Grammar School

TELEVISION

I come in different colours,
different sizes, different shapes.

I'm put in different cupboards,
different rooms, different spaces.

I am known by everyone as a box
with pictures.

I respond, reply, request in
many different ways.

I cunningly get people to watch
addictively.

I am the most watched and listened to

Yet nobody knows me.

I am not allowed to move except
within myself.

Everyone laughs, cries and looks at me.

I am the one true entertainer.

I am the *television*.

Bernie Collins (13)
Mount Lourdes Grammar School

LIKES

There I lie in my comfy bed,
As snug as a bug in a rug.
Mum tucks Ted and I up
And gives me a great big hug.

In the darkness, I lie dreaming
Of Berger, Fowler and Owen
Scored once, scored twice.
'Don't miss the penalty,' I groan.

In my dreams, they're the Champions
No doubt they'll win the Cup
With my hero in top form
They're on the up, up, up.

The chant goes up, a thunderous applause
'You'll never walk alone' keeps beating,
A wonderful match, a fine duet
Sung by Shania Twain and Ronan Keating.

What more could I ask,
A winning match, a striking pair,
Down to earth I come
As the alarm bell fills the air.

Oh, how I hate that noise
Ringing in my head,
Don't make me get up,
I'm warm and snug in my bed.

Clare Harris (11)
Mount Lourdes Grammar School

LOVE

I twist among the people's lives,
Scattering my hopes and dreams among them
Sometimes I take years to develop
In these people's hearts.
Sometimes I just take a glance
I glide gracefully through their happy days together
But sometimes I trip and fall
Though I'm almost always able to get back up.
As their love grows, I prance playfully among them
Manoeuvring myself through their hopes and dreams
Gliding, sliding and slipping among them.
When they are true, I go to new hopefuls
As I know I can never die inside them.

Carla Cassidy (13)
Mount Lourdes Grammar School

THE BREEZE

It swayed with all the branches
It glided over the sea
It scrambled under every gap
And it waltzed with every tree.

It bashed against the windows
It banged on every door
It hurried down the corridors
And it roamed along the moors.

Now the breeze just lingers
Above every boy and girl
Watching, waiting wistfully
To pounce once more again.

Amanda Loughlin (14)
Mount Lourdes Grammar School

RADIO

I am the one who people listen to,
I am the one that nobody cares for.
I yelp and yell but still no one answers
Unless they are singing along with me.
I pray and I plead that someone
will care for me.
But I shiver and feel all alone.
Sometimes I dance along with the music,
But I have to move very quietly
Because the 'people' don't know that I'm there.
I whistle and wonder of the days that used to be,
Of my family and friends that were all around me.
If it wasn't for them who took me away
I'd still be happy to this very day.

Aoife McGovern (13)
Mount Lourdes Grammar School

THE WIND

I swerve around corners,
glide down the street,
pushing or pulling things that I meet.
I drift or dash among people.
They shiver as I go by.
After a while I'm still around
they retire and go inside.
I can whistle and whisper to the trees,
I can blow the curtains with a small breeze.
I am strong in winter, I bring the snow.
I am weak in the summer so I go slow.
The power I have can change as seasons go.

Brenda Rice (13)
Mount Lourdes Grammar School

SUNSHINE

People come to sit in my presence,
In the shade they hide from me,
In the rain they long for me,
I rest at midday for just a minute,
and then I speedily rush on,
I've wasted enough time,
I've got too many places to reach.
I can make damp places dry and dusty
I can scorch skins,
and help to produce plants but
you've got to be patient.
At night I rest for some,
And only just begin for others.

Anne McBrien (14)
Mount Lourdes Grammar School

SNOW

The small white balls of fluff, fly and float,
across the sky, slowly and softly.
It covers the earth in a very big blanket
to keep it nice and warm.
It hurries to get its job done
before the sun comes back again.
It brings great pleasure to the hearts
of the children everywhere.
To watch it twist and twirl all day
is a brilliant sight to see,
But when the sun comes back again,
it slowly fades away.

Claire Reilly (14)
Mount Lourdes Grammar School

AUTUMN

As we say farewell to summer,
Autumn is round the corner,
The long summer nights,
Followed by the short thunderous nights.

Again and again we see the fairies dance,
Wearing their brown and golden dresses,
Fluttering down from the trees above,
They know that we are enjoying the show.

Powerful winds, stormy seas, thunderous nights,
Are all part of this wonderful season,
As the leaves begin to float away
Winter is round the corner.

Caitlin McCann (11)
Mount Lourdes Grammar School

SCARED

As I lay in my bed of a cold winter's night,
the howling wind gave me a terrible fright.
Its howl began low but grew louder and louder,
as the sheets of my bed were pulled higher and higher.

Then all of a sudden, nothing was heard
silence everywhere, I felt so scared.
Then all of a sudden, the light was switched on,
'twas my mother. 'What is wrong?'
'Nothing,' I answered, with a sigh of relief
turned on my side and went back to sleep.

Laura Hannigan
Mount Lourdes Grammar School

BUT

Most people say I'm tidy but I
just know I'm not.
All my friends say I'm good at dancing
but it's two left feet I've got.
Mummy says I'm always happy
but I seem to cry a lot.

My cousin thinks I'm really cool
but I'm copying someone else.
Daddy thinks TV's my life but
having fun is more important.
All my family think I'm clearing out
the fridge but I'm really tidying up.

Tara Jayne Duffy (12)
Mount Lourdes Grammar School

DREAMS

They usually come just out of the blue
We cannot plan them, or make them come true.

Sometimes they are scary!
Sometimes they are sweet!
Sometimes they make us feel like a freak!

I have often had one which I wanted to last,
But others make me glad that I wake up fast.
Sometimes I would like to go back and recap,
But I usually end up just taking a nap.

Charlene McCauley (11)
Mount Lourdes Grammar School

PEACE!

I hear the drums of war
Beating and beating in my ear.
When will it end?
Think peace. Think harmony.
No more hunger.
No more war.
No more bombs.
No more murders.
Just *peace!*

Does there have to be sadness in the world?
Is it really so hard to stop war?
Can I stop it on my own?
I didn't think so.
So help me to make *peace!*

Seana Higgins (11)
Mount Lourdes Grammar School

THE LAST MOMENTS

When we are dying, our lives have faded,
Our swollen hearts disintegrated.
The sadness in our now dull eyes,
Those special moments we memorise.

The times when we knew it was too late,
The last moments begin to disorientate.
Slowly we recognise the last blink of our eyes,
We wish everyone the best and whisper our goodbyes.

Leanne Sweeney (11)
Mount Lourdes Grammar School

CHANGE

In summer my garden is green.
Fresher than new love, it is clean,
And sings to me as I work at my window
I hear its chorus on the breezes that blow
In from colder, harsher places
To enjoy our warmth and our kindly faces.

The sky is blue and birds fly high above
On currents of cool, fresh air that love
To swoop down and kiss my pale cheek
With the voices of the birds, the air is thick,
And they comfort me with the knowledge
That it is man's gift to always pull back from the edge.

Yet summer does end, and the birds all flee
With the warm breezes from the cold to see
Other lands to the south, where the sun is still hot.
My garden withers and its pure green heart is shot
Full with doubt and worry, death and pain
I only realise now that things never remain the same.

Things grow old and depart from the Earth,
Trees, grass, flowers, and people all know death.
They all feel the same old hurt that is at the end
Of all things. Even love dies, weary and spent,
And full of cracks that do nothing but grow
And grow, and eventually destroys the whole.

Peter Strong (15)
Portadown College

THE NIGHT TRAIN

The night train is a lion that roars
through the night,
His powerful body
impressing all he passes.

He pierces the night with
his yellow eyes,
and all the earth trembles
when he rushes past.

Fuelled with energy,
he powers on like lightning.
He sounds ferocious
and he looks so frightening.

Adelle McCarney (14)
St Brigid's High School, Omagh

THE SEA

I lick the shore,
I roll on the sand.
Kids love me, they roar and shout,
As in my edges they splash about.

My silence is the silence of the grave,
My anger is the roar of the lion.
My happiness is a thunderous applause,
My fear is a swell to and fro.
People laugh and they cry,
They live and they die,
But I go on forever like a never-ending song.

Roisin Madden (13)
St Brigid's High School, Omagh

ROMANTIC LOVE

I have the power to melt hearts.
I touch both male and female.
No one sees me but they feel my presence
The moment I strike, life changes.

I bring joy and happiness.
I know people like having me there,
People seek me, I am not hard to find,
I must be treated well to survive.

I am soft, sweet and gentle,
I am in everyone's dreams,
I am something that is felt when
                         two people meet
I am romantic *love*.

Melanie Warren (13)
St Brigid's High School, Omagh

WIND

I hear her at my window,
She rustles and roars and rants and raves,
I always wonder who or what has angered her.
'Clang,' 'bang' she has just thrown a can at the door,
I give myself a shake and I snuggle up into my bed sheets
hoping she won't invade my room through cracks or seams,
I can't get to sleep for now her friend 'Rain' has joined her.
I hear dogs howling, trees swishing and cars driving through puddles.
The lights in the hall go off, everybody is in bed.
I listen again but she has stopped, there is no noise just a gentle breeze.
Thank goodness she has subsided
I close my eyes relieved and fall asleep.

Lynn McCullagh (14)
St Brigid's High School, Omagh

FIRE

My warmth delights
With flames and shapes.
I bring smiles to cold faces,
As they greet me,
Enjoying my different colours and shapes.
Dancing to the sounds.

With my fierce colours and roaring sounds,
Lighting every dark corner of the lonely room
Stretching my unusual arms and legs,
Reaching out to touch.

Useful in those cold, bleak days,
I am a welcoming friend.
Roaring and flickering
From a peaceful candle to a vast blaze.
Quickly spreading, walking
But, soon I become no use.
No light, no warmth.
Slowly, slowly, burning out.

Claire Donaghy (13)
St Brigid's High School, Omagh

WHITE

A calm and relaxing feeling
Snowflakes falling gently
Through the clean frosty air
That Christmas feeling
Peaceful thoughts bringing contentment
Fluffy clouds floating through the sky
Crisp clean sheets drying gently in the wind.

Mary Nugent (13)
St Brigid's High School, Omagh

WHEN I GROW UP

When I grow up, I'd spend my day
In a very special way,

The career that I would like to reach
Is the best of all, I'd like to teach

Of knowledge I would plant the seeds
Especially with children of special needs

'Good morning children' I would say
Call the register to start the day

Get to work and have some fun
Go outside and see the sun

Music, sounds and colours bright
Drama, acting, lots of light

Special children whom God has blessed
I think to teach would be the best

I think it would be very grand
Teaching children, who don't understand.

Laura Martin (11)
St Brigid's High School, Omagh

DEATH

I am a dark cloud overhead
Circling above you all
Each one in turn will receive a call from me.
Some may not see me approaching
To others I am a constant threat.

I watch over you all day
Even when you are asleep.
No matter how long you shall live,
I will be your constant companion.

Silently watching,
Occasionally thinking of when I might strike.
Foolish people dismiss me from their minds.

You have been warned,
Your day will come
Treasure your every moment
Because there is no escape.

Eimear Teague (13)
St Brigid's High School, Omagh

CAT'S EYES

Oh how I look so bright in the night.
How I dazzle like beaming, flashing lights.
I do not take on a person,
but stand out like cats' eyes.
As those so nearly nasty,
the startled eyes frighten people as they turn
A dark, dusty, corner.

When people look deep into my eyes
they hear well, they think they hear the loud
'miaow' sound I make.
I make it especially when I move,
so supple and slow, moving around their legs.

Cats what are we?
We're slim and slender and, as black as coal.

We have nine lives as for you only have one.
So think of it this way.
What if you weren't pin pointing your eyes
on the road.
Where would you be?

Katherine Turbett (13)
St Brigid's High School, Omagh

THE STORM

I am the beast
That makes you shiver in your bed.
My roar of thunder,
My flash of lightning,
My means of attack.

I am fierce.
Windows rattle when I command,
Doors bang.
I am all powerful.

I am the drum of nature,
I am the flash of life,
I am the howling wind,
I am the storm.

Tanya McBride (13)
St Brigid's High School, Omagh

JUST ANOTHER DREAM

I woke up this morning,
there was peace and harmony,
no more racism or hatred,
love filled everyone's hearts!
No more violence,
No more hunger anywhere in the world,
no more painful dying,
But then, I really woke up this morning,
to sadly realise,
it was just another dream,
a hopeful dream.

Lisa McCallion (13)
St Brigid's High School, Omagh

THE STORM

I am a ferocious lion,
Brutal and rough.
I roll and pounce on my prey,
Striking something different every day.
Destroying buildings, trees and homes,
If you are caught, there is no escaping my claws.
People always fear me,
They know to stay inside if I am near.
I cause people a lot of pain,
Attempts to defeat me are always in vain.
People don't know when I will appear,
So beware,
Wherever you may be
I'll be your constant companion.

Roisin Coyle (14)
St Brigid's High School, Omagh

FRIDAYS

The bell has rung, you have to go in,
To an atmosphere that is very dim.
People sit and slouch around,
It's amazing they don't end up on the ground.

The first and second classes are a drag,
The third and fourth should be kept in a bag.

All in all there is no more,
Why is school on Friday such a bore?
The last class you count away the minutes
The bell rings the children roar
'Thank God it's Friday,'
And rush out the door.

Josie Devlin (13)
St Brigid's High School, Omagh

THE DARK

I am a creature of the night,
And when the sun sets I arise.
I unfold my gloomy cloak,
Before your very eyes.

I chase the children all inside,
And call my friends to rise.
The badgers, owl, the fox and bats,
Come out and rub their eyes.

I wander through the park,
I whisper to the trees.
I glide over waterfalls,
And skip through leaves.

As time goes on my cloak gets black,
The night belongs to me.
And everywhere my footsteps go,
Then only I can see.

And often I am chased away,
By shiny lights and lamps.
But never does it spoil my fun,
As I do my merry dance.

Until the sun begins to rise,
And sends me off to bed.
And as the world is waking up,
I lie down to rest my head.

Frances Campbell (13)
St Brigid's High School, Omagh

SNOW

Along the cold curvy kerb
lies a rough and jagged sheet,
A sheet of white wispy snow
That will frostbite your feet.

Beside the park wall
Stands a man who is dark and tall,
As he salts the curly kerbs
He will help you walk along.

Snowmen here - Snowmen there
In the snow you see,
Different sharp and short shapes
you love to watch and stare.

But most of all
you need not care, because you
have not yet experienced
a nasty hurting fall.

Now it's gone for a little while
But you will not yet know,
when the snow decides once again
to fall on your garden wall!

Denise Bradley (13)
St Brigid's High School, Omagh

FROST

I am a winter person, my name is Jack,
I come out in the dark of night,
I tiptoe around turning things white,
I hate colour, everything that is fun,
I especially hate warmth and happiness.

I fill live with misery,
Freezing things here and there casting my spell
My night work is done, the gleam of dawn is ahead
The world awakes and shivers out of bed.

My artistry will remain but not for too long.
It will perish in the rising temperatures of daylight,
My spectacle will soon disappear,
All my work will be wiped away.

I will prepare for the next night.
I will return, of that you can be sure.
I have a duty to perform and I will leave my mark.

My beauty will leave you spellbound.
My bite will strike beware.

Stephanie Duddy (13)
St Brigid's High School, Omagh

WHAT A NIGHT

The night was so full of excitement,
The bonfire was lit,
Children all dressed up,
Now they were told to sit.

The parents took over,
To do the fireworks
Big ones, small ones, dull ones, bright ones.

The children were so happy,
To see the bright colours,
Lighting up the sky in such a night,
Red, blue, pink and green

What a night it must have been!

Clodagh Hagan (14)
St Brigid's High School, Omagh

PAIN

Pain is a hungry monster,
strong and powerful
trapped in its cage.
Minute by minute he throbs and heaves,
he won't lie down.
He's like a volcano waiting to erupt.

Upon release he shivers and shakes,
surges through his
victim trying to
consume him completely,
craving satisfaction.

His victim fights back
by feeding him powerful drugs
which stun him,
forcing him back
urging him to retreat.
The mighty monster
slinks away but
prepares himself for
another attack.

Arlene McCollum (13)
St Brigid's High School, Omagh

What I Would Like To Be When I Grow Up

I would like to be a footballer and score a wining goal.
I would like to be a vet and operate on a foal.

I would like to be an artist and draw in a book
I would like to be a chef and eat what I cook.

I would like to be a pilot and fly to far off lands
I would like to be a popstar and sing with famous bands.

I would like to be a teacher and teach in primary school
I would like to be a lifeguard and save children at the pool.

I'd like to be a baker and bake up lots of bread
I'd like to be a doctor I would put my patients all to bed.

I'd like to be a barmaid behind some fancy bars
I'd like to be an astronaut and travel to the stars.

I'd like to be a fashion queen and wear the latest styles
I'd like to be a lawyer with my office filled with files.

Donna Maguire (12)
St Brigid's High School, Omagh

Red

A warm fire glowing on cold nights
Anger ready to burst out
Embarrassment colouring my face
Warning of danger ahead
A beautiful sunset on a summer's evening
A shiny apple
A juicy strawberry.

Danielle Moore (13)
St Brigid's High School, Omagh

MY ANIMAL HOUSE

I have a dog, a jolly little dog.
He is old and moves quite slowly.
He barks quite a lot, I love him.
He is particular about what food he eats.
He has really blue eyes I call him Granda.

I have a pedigree racing pigeon,
He eats good quality corn and is strong and healthy.
He sits on his perch and coos all day long.
On racing day he uses his homing instinct
to win the race. I call him Daddy.

I have a cat,
She is small and very friendly.
She moves quickly and is very lively.
She is quite a crazy character.
She purrs most of the time.
I call her my sister.

Tracy Sharkey (12)
St Brigid's High School, Omagh

SCHOOL'S OUT

I wake up each morning and hate to hear
My mum saying it's time to get up dear
I hate walking through that door
Having to go to English, oh, what a bore
I wish I had free classes all day
Getting to talk to my friends and hear what they have to say
I just can't wait until twenty-past three
Just five more minutes and I'll be home free
Thank God school's out!

Ann Coyle (13)
St Brigid's High School, Omagh

THE GALE

The gale is a lion
it roars as it roams,
sending everything
scurrying and flying about
to get in its clutches could be fatal
it needs to be treated with respect

With its tireless jaws it lashes out,
throwing the heaviest of things about
its roars and howls can be easily heard
bringing fear to the night

Its strength and power it likes to show,
worry and alarm spreading
like the small in the wild
we have to lie low praying we will escape.

Joanne Campbell (13)
St Brigid's High School, Omagh

WAR OR PEACE?

How does it help?
Killing each other,
Breaking hearts and bringing tears to everyone.
What is the point?
We are getting nowhere at
The end of the long, dark, dismal day!
All we can do now is,
Hope and pray that peace
Comes to us!
Everyone in the world wants it
Why can't we have it?

Fionnula Haughey (14)
St Brigid's High School, Omagh

DEATH!

I am an eagle,
I swoop and capture my prey.
As swift as the breeze I'll kill one by one,
Either father, mother, daughter or son.

When I catch I never release,
You'll be buried down beneath.
Just when you think you're safe,
I'll attack with a colds embrace.

You'll never escape,
Attempts will be futile.
For I am as strong as a rock
And have a heart of stone.

No one can ever defeat me,
Not man or beast alone.
I will go but I will be back,
Beware death lies down your track.

Majella Maguire (14)
St Brigid's High School, Omagh

SUN

I am the sun shining bright in the sky,
My rays can be dangerous
Watch you might fry,
But if you are careful and take good care
Let me be your friend and
I will give plenty of warm air,
So take my advice and you won't go wrong,
But enjoy my warmth all day long.

Donna Treanor (13)
St Brigid's High School, Omagh

WHEN I GROW UP

I'd like to be a hairdresser, with scissors brush and comb,
I'd like to be a captain and sail upon the foam

I'd like to be a vet, with horses, dogs and cats,
I'd like to be a clothes designer, make skirts, dresses and hats.

I'd like to be an artist, draw pictures for the walls,
I'd like to be a toy maker, make cars, teddies and dolls.

I'd like to be an author and write exciting stories,
I'd like to be a fish keeper and sell you some John Dories.

I'd like to be a barmaid pulling drink to the brink,
I'd like to be a lifeguard, saving people when they sink.

I'd like to be a popstar and sing the night away,
I'd like to be a guide and lead people on their way.

I'd like to be a teacher, be cross with every child,
I'd like to be a zoo keeper and look after the wild.

I'd like to be a skater and skate upon the rink,
I'd like to be just everything just everything I think.

Sinéad Monaghan (11)
St Brigid's High School, Omagh

OUR EARTH

It sparkles, it shines,
stands out from the rest,
it brings mysteries and joyfulness,
secrets hidden, locked up in a chest.

Blue sparkles like a diamond,
a dark trace of green
a blue jewel
it was called when first seen.

So round so beautiful,
through treated with disrespect,
with CFCs and mobile phones,
what will be the effect?

Will the sparkle disappear,
the mysteries be solved,
secrets known,
the Earth stop being revolved?

Kerri McCusker (13)
St Brigid's High School, Omagh

FIRE

Behind a grate I am controlled,
Behind a door my claws are stalled.
People sit quite close to me
When I am calm and anger free.

When folk are careless
And let me roam
I do great damage to their home
I destroy all things in my path
For I care not, I unleash my wrath.

When finally, I am really free
And running wild among the trees
No living thing will I spare
For life and limp I have no care
I devour with great appetite
And all your efforts I will fight
Only one thing I do fear
And that is water cool and clear.

Mairéad Gormley (13)
St Brigid's High School, Omagh

FIRE!

I am a roaring fire.
I am as red as blood and as hot as
the fires from Hell.
I may appear to be gentle or
As mad and ferocious as a wild dog.
I can toss, tear and tumble all in
front of me,
I am a roaring fire,
But when I am gentle,
I am warm like the rays from the sun.
I can comfort and cuddle and
I can cool down,
Because I am a roaring fire and I
am in *control!*

Donna Conway (14)
St Brigid's High School, Omagh

A MOTHER'S LOVE

She covers me like a blanket,
From the cold rain,
When I look into her eyes
I know her love is real
For me every day,
Her love will never end,
And I'm thankful for everything
Thou hast done for me in my life
The one my love is for
Is my dear mother forever,
All I want you to know is that my
Love will never end.

Clare Conlin (12)
St Brigid's High School, Omagh

THE ANIMAL HOUSE

I have a mouse, a fury, small mouse,
She is cautious and speedy,
She runs if she sees me and squeaks.
She eats cheese most of the day,
I call her Toni.

I have a parrot, a bright chirpy parrot,
She has colourful feathers and natters non-stop,
When she flies she is like a rainbow with wings.
She eats and spits out nuts all day,
I call her Clara.

I have a monkey, a naughty monkey,
She has a brown furry coat.
She deliberately gets herself into trouble.
She eats bananas and spits them at people,
I call her my baby sister Bronagh.

Kirsty Gormley (12)
St Brigid's High School, Omagh

MILLENNIUM

Coming close to another year,
to celebrate, have fun and have nothing to fear.
Only this time it's special, important and new,
it's the millennium - yes it's true.

Celebrations, parties, fun galore,
something to remember forever more.
I don't know about you - but I can't wait,
I'm really looking forward to it - it's going to be great!

5, 4, 3, 2, 1 - it's the millennium, here we come!

Kelly Devlin (13)
St Brigid's High School, Omagh

METAPHORS

I have a kangaroo, a hairy kangaroo,
She likes hopping about,
If I pick on her she pounces on me,
I call her my sister Neamh.

I have an Alsatian, a fierce Alsatian,
She knows everything about my life,
She can be nice but also fierce,
If I annoy her she digs her paws into me,
I call her my sister Eimhear,

I know a cat, a very sneaky cat,
He sneaks about every minute of the day,
He cares for me and looks over me,
I call him Dad.

I know a dove, a caring dove,
She cares for me every minute of the day,
She helps me go through life easily,
I call her Mum.

Dearbhla Woods (12)
St Brigid's High School, Omagh

SOUND

You can't feel me,
You can't see me,
But you can hear me.

I can be quite,
I can be loud,
I can be creepy,
I can be peaceful.

On the dark nights
I can scare you,
On the lonely nights
I can comfort you.

Every move you make,
I will be there.
Everywhere you go,
I will be heard.
I am sound.

Siobhan Galbraith (14)
St Brigid's High School, Omagh

THE ANIMAL HOUSE

I have a swan, with a very slim neck,
She squabbles away whether you listen or not,
She moves gracefully from room to room
Tidying up,
I call her Mum.

I have a gorilla with a very round belly,
He roars as if he runs the house,
He moves quickly from place to place,
He has a very hairy body,
I call him Dad.

I have a mouse with very short legs,
He's very cheeky when he's looking for cheese,
He moves very quickly all through the house,
He's a very impish little mouse,
I call him my brother.

Ciara Gallagher (12)
St Brigid's High School, Omagh

THE ANIMAL HOUSE

I have a bee, a very buzzy bee.
She flies around the house continuously working.
She's sometimes calm.
She cares a lot for her young, I call her Mum.

I have a dog, a very noisy dog.
He barks very loudly at his young.
He works outside all day long.
He runs around the house. I call him Dad.

I have a swan, a very calm swan.
She is always helping me.
She cares for old people in a home
And is always kind to me. I call her my sister.

Leona O'Neill (13)
St Brigid's High School, Omagh

FEAR

I can appear when you least expect me,
You don't always see me, but you can feel my presence.
In the dead of the night I wonder freely,
In thoughts racing uncontrolled.

I have great power,
To make your heart thump, make your teeth chatter.

I am both good and evil,
I have the power to make you run from a stranger
And I can paralyse you on the spot like a block of ice.

I am as a ghost always there to haunt you.

I am fear.

Nicola Glass (13)
St Brigid's High School, Omagh

THE ANIMAL HOUSE

I have a bear, an ugly hairy bear,
He roars at you for doing something wrong,
He has big feet and long nails,
He eats all day, I call him Dad.

I have a swan,
She is a beautiful, gentle, pretty thing,
She is very caring and looks after her young all the time,
She is a very hard worker,
I call her Mum.

I have a dog,
She is a very cheeky and bad mannered eating her dinner,
She looks very cute and pretty and she stands wagging her tail,
She is very playful and very happy,
I call her my little sister.

Geraldine Nugent (12)
St Brigid's High School, Omagh

CREATURES

When I look outside I see
the creatures on the window
looking in at me,
I look again and see leaves falling
off the trees, stumps of roots
and conkers, on the ground,
frogs jumping around,
but all I love to see is
all the creatures flying in the sky or
all the plants in the garden.

Tanya Hughes (11)
St Brigid's High School, Omagh

What Would You Like To Be When You Grow Up, Little Girl?

I'd like to be an Irish dancer and dance upon that stage,
I'd like to be an artist and draw pictures on a page.

I'd like to be a hairdresser and chop off everyone's hair,
I'd like to be an air hostess and fly up in the air.

I'd like to be an astronaut and fly up in a rocket,
I'd like to be a millionaire and have money in my pocket.

I'd like to be a teacher and teach little ones,
I'd like to be a famous person on the front of The Sun.

I'd like to be a presenter and present the Bill,
I'd like to be a joiner and have a little drill.

Orla Byrne (11)
St Brigid's High School, Omagh

Tornado

I rush through the country
And nothing can stop me,
Everyone fears me
In a blink I am there,

Trees collapse at my will,
I demand cars to fly.
Commander of all
I invade and destroy.

Twisting and spinning,
So recklessly alive.
Throwing and hurling
Until exhausted I die.

Marie Lynch (14)
St Brigid's High School, Omagh

What I Would Like To Be When I Grow Up

I'd like to be a cook cooking up the stew;
I'd like to be a dinner lady watching while they queue;

I'd like to be a policewoman walking on the beat;
I'd like to be a patrol woman always on the street;

I'd like to be a hairdresser making you look smart;
I'd like to be a farmer going to the mart;

I'd like to be a nurse making you feel well;
I'd like to be a sexton and ring the church bell;

I'd like to be a cooper making all the barrels;
I'd like to be a baker baking soda farls;

I'd like to be a cobbler mending lots of shoes;
I'd like to be a news caster reading out the news;

I'd like to be an air hostess flying high for weeks;
I'd like to be a plumber fixing all the leaks;

I'd like to be a cleaner shining all the pots;
I'd like to be a photographer taking all the shots;

I'd like to be an actress meeting all the stars;
I'd like to be a soldier fighting in the wars;

I'd like to be a DJ turning up the sound;
I'd like to be a bus driver taking you to town.

Catherine Conway (11)
St Brigid's High School, Omagh

My Animal House

I have a monkey a small nosed monkey
who chatters around the house,
he is very sneaky but is always caught
climbing up to the banana cupboard,
he's usually in his room
I call him my older brother.

I have a hamster who goes squeaking
around the house, she's scurrying around
the house working from time to time and
also nosying in my bag, I call her Mum.

I have a giraffe a very tall one,
he's only in the house in the evening
he's always messing around with me,
he walks around the house with his back bent over
and always knows how to make me laugh,
I call him Dad.

Kellie McKenna (12)
St Brigid's High School, Omagh

What I Want To Be

I want to be a news reader, smart and clean;
I'd like to be a midwife kind and not mean.

I want to be a singer, rich and definitely not poor;
I'd like to be a saleswoman, going from door to door.

I want to be a jockey, fast and not slow;
I'd like to be a baker, baking lots of dough.

I'd like to be a dancer, in the Riverdance;
I'd like to be a zoologist and work with lots of ants.

I'd like to be a pianist, pressing lots of keys;
I'd like to be a beekeeper, working with buzzing bees.

I'd like to be a teacher giving people lots of books;
I'd like to be a beautician giving people new looks.

Joanne O'Brien (11)
St Brigid's High School, Omagh

ANIMAL HOUSE

I have a bear, a hairy faced bear,
He's big and strong and in control.
He works hard and when I annoy him he growls,
But when I need him he's warm and gentle
I call him Dad.

I have a swan, she's very elegant and graceful,
And very hard working.
She advises me on what to do in life,
She also provides for me and protects me.
I call her Mum.

I have a peacock, and she is very proud,
She always looks after her appearance.
She always has to be neat and tidy and looking perfect
I call her my big sister.

Gemma McGlone (12)
St Brigid's High School, Omagh

WHEN I GROW UP

When I grow up someday soon,
I'd like to spin
off to the moon.

I could be a nurse
with my uniform and cap,
I'd tuck up grannies
for their afternoon nap.

I'd like to be a teacher
with my books and chalk
I'd scold the children
who will talk and talk.

I'll own a fiddle
and play all day,
I'll be my own boss
and rest when I say.

Kathryn Conwell (12)
St Brigid's High School, Omagh

WHEN I GROW UP

When I grow up
I could be a gardener
to grow lots of plants and trees

I could be a sailor
to sail the Seven Seas
to look for mermaids near the sea

I could be a hairdresser
to design people's hair

Of all the nice things there are to be
When I grow up I'll choose
the one that's just for me.

Nicola Fiddis (11)
St Brigid's High School, Omagh

WHEN I GROW UP I WANT TO BE . . .

When I grow up I think
I'll be a vet and jag a needle
in loads of people's pets.

I could be a soldier or
join the Navy but I think
I'll chicken out and leave
that a maybe.

I think I'll be a chiropodist
but I think there would be a smell
so I could be a dentist
and do that just as well

But of all of these jobs
I hold a little grudge
so when I grow up, I'll really be
a judge.

Fiona Kelly (12)
St Brigid's High School, Omagh

PRIMARY SCHOOL!

In primary one, of course you can have fun.
In primary two, I learned how to tie my shoe.
In primary three, I fell and hurt my knee!
In primary four, I was knocking on heaven's door.
In primary five, I was hardly, barely alive.
In primary six, I was counting tally sticks.
In primary seven, I was in heaven,
But don't be a fool and act all cool, or you'll be the fool.
You enjoyed the seven years,
There might be some little tears,
It's not so bad so give them a hand.
All the effort we put through,
Tying our shoes in primary two.
That's all for two days throwing all them seven years away.

Leon Murphy (11)
St Brigid's High School, Omagh

MY ANIMAL HOUSE

I have a bear, a scary bear.
He protects his family from danger.
He sometimes gets cross with me and my brother.
He has a powerful walk. I call him Dad.

I also have a monkey.
A very cheeky monkey. He always annoys and pesters me.
He chatters a lot. He is away most of the time.
I call him my brother.

I also have a giraffe.
He is very tall and noisy. He also annoys me a lot.
He never stops eating. He can reach very big trees
With his long neck. I call him my big brother.

Emma Deazley (12)
St Brigid's High School, Omagh

THE ANIMAL HOUSE

I have a bear, a scary looking bear.
He protects his family all year round.
He never gets cross with me.
He walks with power. I call him Dad.

I have a swan, a pretty swan.
She looks after her family night and day.
She gracefully glides about all day.
She is a beautiful swan. I call her Mum.

I have a monkey, a very cheeky monkey.
He always pesters me and he chatters all day.
He jumps about from tree to tree.
He is a nice monkey. I call him Brother.

I have a crocodile, a fierce crocodile.
She protects her property
And she danders about all day.
She looks at me crossly, I call her Sis.

Aileen Devine (12)
St Brigid's High School, Omagh

GREEN

My turtle swimming in his tank.
Those horrible vegetables my mother is
always telling me to eat.
The hills in the countryside.
The sign on the traffic lights signalling go.
When I'm on a boat and feel seasick.
The cows munching away in the field.
The colour of my country from far in space.

Jade Devine (13)
St Brigid's High School, Omagh

To The Rhythm

My mates and I we like to party.
Every night - eight to late,
All day long, we just can't wait,
To hear the music and get that beat.

Let's get going,
Let's go out,
It's time to get grooving
While the DJs are out.

It's time to get glammed up
Time to party on down,
You've got the beat
Move your body around.

You gotta hear the dance vibes,
They're thumping and pumping,
I said get on that floor,
You'd better get jumping.

The night's nearly gone,
But we'll have to do the same.
Tomorrow's Saturday night,
We'll start all over again.

Chereen McGoldrick (14)
St Brigid's High School, Omagh

My Baby Brother

He is like a cheerful lamb jumping around,
So bubbly he is making a lot of sound.

Cute and cuddly like my teddy bear,
With chubby red cheeks and fair coloured hair.

Sparkling blue eyes that stand out a mile,
His perfect new teeth create a white smile.

At the centre of his face is a button nose,
At the end of his feet are fat little toes.

Sitting at the dinner table with dinner everywhere,
Getting himself dirty as if he doesn't care.

He is dearly loved and cherished by everyone,
A perfect little brother, and a perfect son.

Charlene Colton (15)
St Brigid's High School, Omagh

I'D LIKE TO BE . . .

I'd like to be an air hostess, and fly around in the air,
I'd like to be a hairdresser, and cut and style your hair.

I'd like to work behind a bar, and serve some people beers,
I'd like to be at Saint Brigid's studying new careers.

I'd like to be a teacher, and work with little ones,
I'd like to serve in a cafe, and put out the nice cream buns.

I'd like to be a model girl, with all the lovely looks,
I'd like to be a perfect cook, and always wanting to cook.

I'd like to be a dancer, and dance to the country beat,
I'd like to be an usherette, and show you to your seat.

I'd like to be a showjumper, and ride around the paddock,
I'd like to be a fish farmer, and cook up some gorgeous haddock.

I'd like to be a chauffeur, and drive an Audi car,
I'd like to be a sailor, and sail a boat afar.

I'd like to be a magician, pulling rabbits out of hats,
I'd like to be a local vet, helping dogs and cats.

        And that's the end of that!

Laura Logue (11)
St Brigid's High School, Omagh

THE ANIMAL HOUSE

I have a bee, a very busy bee.
She works all day,
She is kind, caring and is there to help her young.
I call her Mum.

I have a monkey, a cute monkey.
He eats a lot of bananas, and also jumps about.
He is active all day.
I call him my young brother.

I have a lion, a big lion.
He's out all day.
He's boss of the house.
I call him Dad.

I have a kitten, a cute kitten,
She drinks a lot of milk.
She crawls, and plays with her toys.
I call her my baby cousin.

Hayley Early (12)
St Brigid's High School, Omagh

YELLOW

The sun is shining in the sky
Brightening up the buttercups
The sand at the seaside
Is glowing very brightly
I gobble down my plate of sweetcorn
Out comes the moon
Away goes the ducks
The street lights light up
And the taxis are parked.

Suzanne Allen (13)
St Brigid's High School, Omagh

My Future

I'd like to be a social worker, to help all those in need,
I'd like to be a gardener, to pull out all those weeds,

I'd like to be a banker, to sort out people's money,
I'd like to be a beekeeper, to make some golden honey,

I'd like to be a dancer, and dance the night away,
I'd like to be in parliament, and really have a say,

I'd like to be a teacher, and teach you all I know,
I'd like to be a doctor, and mend your broken toe,

I'd like to be an air hostess, to travel near and far,
I'd like to be an actress, and become a famous star,

I'd like to be a model, and walk upon the stage,
I'd like to be a writer, and fill every page,

I'd like to be a gymnast, and swing from bar to bar,
I'd like to be a grand chauffeur, and drive a fancy car,

I'd like to be an usherette, and show you to your row,
I'd like to be a funny clown, and wear a dotty bow,

I'd like to be a skater, skating round and round,
I'd like to be a DJ, and pump out all those sounds,

I'd like to be a hairdresser, and wear my hair just right,
I'd like to be a lady wrestler, to get stuck into a fight.

Laura Galbraith (12)
St Brigid's High School, Omagh

What I Want To Be When I Grow Up!

I'd like to be a beautician, and give you a good face.
I'd like to be a runner, and have a good old pace.

I'd like to be a TV star, and make a move or two.
I'd like to be a doctor, and have a look at you.

I'd like to be a singer, and sing the songs so smooth.
I'd like to be a Romany, and always be on the move.

I'd like to be a banker, and give your money to you.
I'd like to be a hairdresser, and cut your hair for you.

I'd like to be an astronaut, and fly off to space.
I'd like to be a canoe racer, and win a good old race.

I'd like to be a barmaid, and serve you up a good old drink.
I'd like to be an ice skater, and race right round the rink.

I'd like to be a news reader, and tell you all the news.
I'd like to be a dinner lady, and serve you up your stew.

I'd like to be a nurse, and earn a lot of money.
I'd like to be a clown, and be very very funny.

I'd like to be a footballer, and kick the ball up the field.
I'd like to be a waitress, and serve you up a good old meal.

Louise Conway (11)
St Brigid's High School, Omagh

MY FAMILY

I have a tiger,
Who is sometimes cross and angry.
He hunts for his family's food,
I call him Dad.

         I have a lovely rabbit
         Who's warm, nice and cuddly,
         She gives me a hug whenever I need one
         I call her Mum.

I have a big dog,
He follows me wherever I go,
He eats everything I give him,
I call him my brother Eóin.

         I have a slithery snake,
         Who fits into any small hole.
         He is so fine and skinny,
         I call him my brother Emmett.

I have a cute little kitten,
Who smiles at you all the time,
He does everything you tell him to do,
I call him my baby brother Oisín.

Shaunéen Cleary (13)
St Brigid's High School, Omagh

HALLOWE'EN

Creepy, scary what a night,
Everything about it gives you a fright.
Fancy dress ghosts, goblins and witches,
They'll all have you in stitches.

As dark as coal or so they say,
Not at all like the month of May.
Games for all, the old and the young,
So join in and have fun.

Bonfires galore and fireworks too,
Be careful in case someone shouts boo!
Shout and screams, oh what a noise,
That's what you get with a crowd of boys.

A pumpkin with an orange glow,
Light its candle, don't be so slow.
Another thing that's scary too
Is bats flying around you.

But when it's all over what a shame,
Then you turn back into being the same.
So say goodbye for now, or so it be,
Haunting, Hallowe'en will come back, you'll see.

Emma McConnell (12)
St Brigid's High School, Omagh

LIFE

Life, what is the meaning of it?
We will all end up in a wooden box underground;
Many are born with the misfortune of being handicapped,
Some people take it upon themselves to abolish this gift of life,
Family and friends are left to control with the grief in their hearts,
Left behind by a loved one,
Starvation and poverty exist,
Yet people would rather waste food and money stupidly.
We take too much for granted,
Wars are fought, men and women alike are killed,
Why?
There seems no answer to this question,
Appreciate what you have, you don't know how long
You'll have it.

Leona Ashenhurst (14)
St Brigid's High School, Omagh

RED

The shiny berries on the holly at Christmas.
Roses that we send on Valentine's Day.
The flames of a blazing hot fire on a cold winter's night.
Signs of danger
Or my mum when she's angry.
Blood when we fall and cut ourselves,
But most of all the velvet suit that Santa wears on Christmas Eve.

Claire Nugent (12)
St Brigid's High School, Omagh

WHITE

The first fluffy snowflake,
A newly built snowman,
The bright glowing stars at night,
The bouncy, drifting clouds at night,
The tummy of a penguin,
The sparkly shine of teeth,
These are my images.

Grainne O'Donnell (12)
St Brigid's High School, Omagh

YELLOW

The fields of corn and buttercups,
The pollen on the flower tops.
The sand, the sun, the moon and stars,
And taxis like banana cars.
The dandelions in the grass,
The ducks upon the pond.
The lemon and the melon all chopped up,
Of which we're very fond.

Laura Fitzgerald (12)
St Brigid's High School, Omagh

MY SCHOOL POEM

From the second I enter to the moment I leave
I hear all the sounds a school could have.
Starting with the bell and moving to the footsteps,
And finally to the thing that keeps my school going,
The sound of talkative girls.

Michelle Havern (11)
St Mary's High School, Newry

A DAY TO REMEMBER

I was waiting in the school hall,
Waiting for my dad to come.
I knew something was wrong
By the tone of sympathy in the teachers' voice.

A home people whispering
and nodding, that's the youngest.
My mother was sitting in a pool
of her own tears crying out angry sighs.
Dad was crying like a baby.

I walked into the room and saw the coffin,
There he was my own brother lying in a box.
Did God have to be this cruel?
Why couldn't it have been different?

Emma Blackadder (14)
St Mary's High School, Newry

HALLOWE'EN

It's Hallowe'en Night
Oh what a fright.
There's hair that's green
And witches' faces to be seen
Knock the door, run if you dare!
Stay, get nuts to share.
Bonfires light up the sky
Rockets go whizzing by,
Bangers that bang,
Children that sang,
Sparklers that crackle
Witches who cackle.

Marie-Claire McAteer (12)
St Mary's High School, Newry

YOU GO IN

You go in, you take a seat,
All you can hear is the noise of feet.
All the tables consist of eight,
You're rushing, you don't want to be late.

Your table's called up,
You're told to stop.
At the end of the queue,
Waiting's all you can do.

You pick your food,
Hoping it's good.
Then pay your money,
Buying bread, and honey.

You then sit down,
There's loads of sounds.
While you eat your meal,
You think, 'Did I get a good deal?'

While the noise of,
Children shouting like bulls charging.
The noise of footsteps like people marching.
Crisping and crunching like leaves outside,
The noise in the hall sounds really wild.

The noise in the hall goes on and on,
Until the bell goes.
Ding! Dang! Ding! Dong.

Going up the stairs,
You think school's a pain,
Because:
You're going to
   Your class
      Again!

Eve Finnegan (11)
St Mary's High School, Newry

HEARTACHE

Those sorrowful years
Crying stress and tears,
Discomfort and heartache
My gentle heart is to break

My feelings have now failed
And so have I
Every night I feel I am ready to cry!

Those cruel, selfish and childish boys and girls,
With roses on their cheeks and curls in their hair.
I have short trousers, T-shirts and socks
They are the things they like to mock!

My mum is by my bedside
Crying with fear.
Tears rolling down her cheeks like waterfalls.
Which I can hear.

Then slowly but solemnly
I fall into a deep sleep
Which no one can take away
This comfort and peace.

Leanne Maguire (11)
St Mary's High School, Newry

GRANDPARENTS

Grandparents, they spoil us with gifts and love
They are like saints from above.
Christmas, birthdays a special treat,
Kind and gentle they're always so sweet.

When Mum and Dad want to go out
They just give Nanny and Grandad a shout.
They're always willing to help in any way
Even having us over to stay.

They are so interesting with stories of long ago,
Fairies and ghosts - where did they all go?
Did they really dance around a fairy ring?
What an eerie feeling this all brings.

They were not spoilt like us children today,
They made their own fun and play.
No drugs to lead them astray
Not like the world we live in today.

I think they deserve a big thank you
For all the kind things that they do.
So Nannies and Grandads we all appreciate you
And thank you again for all that you do.

Julie-Anne Franks (15)
St Mary's High School, Newry

I REMEMBER

I remember when I was young,
I always sat and sucked my thumb.
I would often climb on every chair,
And throw everything up into the air.

As I got older I started playschool,
It was different, you had to play by the rules.
Then I grew older and had a lot of friends,
But I hope today that friendship never ends.

Cara O'Hagan (12)
St Mary's High School, Newry

FRIDAY NIGHTS

It's the end of the school week,
And I can't wait,
To go out and party with my mates.
Dancing and singing,
Talking and ringing,
At last it's Friday night.

We grab the taxi and pay our fare,
I hope the boys like my hair.
My make-up's done,
Let's have some fun,
At last it's Friday night.

Thank God we got in,
The party's just beginning.
The music is pumping,
We all start jumping.
At last it's Friday night.

The night is over,
We had a great time.
We're now going home,
I'll do it all again.
I can't wait till Friday night.

Brenda Kerr (15)
St Mary's High School, Newry

ST MARY'S SCHOOL, SIGHTS AND SOUNDS

Assembly at nine, I'm feeling fine,
Class starts soon in another room.
Down the corridors we all stroll,
And there is the teacher marking the roll.

The lunchtime bell rings really loud,
All around there's a lot of sound.
Girls all meeting up in crowds,
All heading to the yard.

At three o'clock home I trek,
I walk away, I don't look back.
I carry home my rucksack,
And try to forget that tomorrow,
I'll be back!

Cheryl Treanor (11)
St Mary's High School, Newry

A MILLENNIUM PARTY

People talking, people dancing
Children singing, grannies prancing.
Champagne glasses clink with joy
The millennium's here - oh boy!

You see the fireworks explode with excitement
As the church bells ring to bring in the new year.

This is a party, a party of fun,
This is a party, a millennium one!

Eilish McParland (14)
St Mary's High School, Newry

Why Tich?

Tich was a little girl
who was not well.
The first time you saw her
this you could tell.

You could see her walking on the path
watching all the children play,
while she just sits lonely
staring away.

She dresses in clothes
too small for her frame,
but your pity goes out to her
all the same.

Her pink-framed glasses
with elastoplast,
her one foot three sizes
bigger than the last.

Tich was left out of a lot of things,
especially school teams
it always seems.

At the age of twelve
poor Tich was taken
to our God above
and we were forsaken.

Joanne Smyth (12)
St Mary's High School, Newry

SIGHTS AND SOUNDS

Another day at school.
Rain is beating off the top of my umbrella
Everyone is running for shelter.
I shake off my umbrella as I open the creaky brown door.
Water drops from my school bag and hair
And my shoes make a squeaky noise on the corridor floor.
There are footsteps all around running in all directions
Everyone is shouting and laughing.
I see pictures and students' awards upon the wall
I enter my classroom just in time for the bell.
It's nine o'clock my schoolday begins.
The teacher enters the classroom and we eventually settle down
to work,
But there are still occasional whispers behind me.
The sun is breaking through the classroom window
The teacher coughs to clear her throat.
School bags rattle and books slam onto the desk
As we begin another day at school.

Grainne Noade (12)
St Mary's High School, Newry

MY LITTLE DOG

I have a little dog
I named her after me.
I take her for a walk each day
And put her on a lead.
We walked down by the river,
We walked down by the trees,
And when I let her off the lead,
She runs away from me.

Judith McAleavey (15)
St Mary's High School, Newry

GRANDPARENTS

What are they like?
Always fussing or busy making tea or cakes
They insist on having the family together at least once a week
But if you can't make it, it will annoy them.

They're always sitting knitting
Or talking about 'the good old days'
They always seem to be losing things
But then finding them again two minutes later.

They always eat 'hard sweets' or 'hot sweets'
And they're always fully stocked up
With chocolate and lemonade.

Nothing's ever any bother to them
They always have time to talk
Although they seem to worry
About heating or losing their keys

Never touch or move around,
Anything belonging to them
Or they'll get flustered and annoyed
And that's not something anyone
Would like to see.
But I guess that's just what makes
Grandparents, grandparents.

Naiomh O'Brien (14)
St Mary's High School, Newry

SIGHTS AND SOUNDS

I'm standing in the corridor,
I'm looking all around.
It's amazing when you listen,
To each and every sound . . .

Chatter, chatter, chatter,
Click, click, click.
Rushing here and rushing there,
Everything so quick . . .

Some girls are busy talking,
While others make no sound.
The choir are singing sweetly,
And it echoes all around . . .

Sometimes when I talk too much,
I simply cannot hear.
All the things that I could learn,
If I listen with my *ear!*

Jennifer Hehir (12)
St Mary's High School, Newry

COUNTRY SMELLS

If you drive out to what they say is
The good old country air.
Then you are hit with
A revolting smell of silage,
More commonly known as dung.

Breathe in that good country air they say,
When all I want to do is close my mouth
And hold my nose to block it out.

In the grassy green fields with the scent of Earth,
Stands a herd of cows leaving trails of manure,
That would lift the head clean from your shoulders.
Steam rising and a waft lingering in the air.

So tell me as you drive through the country and inhale,
What smells so good about the country air?

Patrice Gorman (12)
St Mary's High School, Newry

SCHOOL SOUNDS

Different uniform
Different rules
Lots of faces
It's a different school

Lots of laughter
Lots of cheer
Just the start
Of my first year

Different teachers
Different chums
A lot of subjects
And the usual sums

Footsteps on the stairways
Footsteps on the halls
All new sounds to me
I'll soon know them all

Jennifer Campbell (11)
St Mary's High School, Newry

GRANDMA'S BEEPER

Grandma! Grandma! Don't despair,
You go sit in your new chair.
You take a nap,
With a beeper at your back.

Eat ice-cream, buns and sweets,
You only get these on special treats.

I'll clean the floor and then
We'll go to the supermarket store.
All of a sudden a fire starts,
But I can't find you, but then I hear *beee-ep!*
When I realised I left you behind at the video store.

Louise Campbell (11)
St Mary's High School, Newry

THE DAY I STARTED ST MARY'S

When I woke up I felt like a bear,
The thought of starting school gave me a nightmare.
When I got to school I saw loads of girls,
Hanging around the stairs.
Some were quiet, some were talking;
As they waited to go to their classes.

We met our teachers,
Who all had different types of features.
It felt so different moving from class to class,
Moving to a different subject all the time.

Cathy Fitzpatrick (12)
St Mary's High School, Newry

WHY ME?

Why am I being bullied?
I didn't do anything wrong.
I feel so scared and alone
And I feel I want to tell.
But I can't, in case they get me.

They call me all sorts of names,
Specky - four eyes and they call me *big ears*
And it hurts and upsets me.

What have I done to deserve this?
I ask myself every day, but I just can't think.
Every day I see them -
My knees shake like a volcano erupting.

Who should I tell?
I don't know, but I have to tell someone quick,
In case it gets any worse.

When is it going to stop?
I don't know, but I hope it's soon.
Very soon!

Oonagh Byrne (13)
St Mary's High School, Newry

CLOUDS

White and fluffy
Different shapes.
Performing in the sky,
As if they were in a race.

Gemma Craven (11)
St Mary's High School, Newry

THE RAIN

It's raining today,
It's no fun because we can't play.
I can't go outside and play on the swings
Or call for my friends to go to the choir and sing.

It's boring outside,
There's nothing to do.
We can't play football,
Boo! Hoo!

Wait!
There's a rainbow in sight,
The sky is getting bright,
The rain has just lost its fight.

Clare-Louise Cookson (11)
St Mary's High School, Newry

AUTUMN

Autumn leaves are falling,
And the trees are getting bare.
The withering leaves pile up each day,
With many colours rare.
There's *brown* and *gold* and *amber*,
Which sparkle after rain.
But soon the colours fade away,
Never to return again.
Till next time around,
The sun of spring brings out the buds again.

Elaine Byrne (11)
St Mary's High School, Newry

BEING A BULLY'S VICTIM

The dismal atmosphere
Fear of breathing
Being controlled by someone else's mind.
Being ostracised and criticised
Grief and despair
Isolated from the crowd.

No friends to comfort you.
No one to understand your fear.
Desperation to know someone who cares,
But no one does!
It's frustrating and aggravating
To be called outrageous names
And feel humiliation.
When will it ever end?
Feeling like a pessimist but -
What else can I be?
Someone help, please!

Eva Keenan (13)
St Mary's High School, Newry

ALL ABOUT SCHOOL

The chittering and chattering of the students in class,
And the stamping that goes up and down the stairs.
The writing of the pens that go up and down,
And the clitter and clatter of all the chairs.
And when the forty minutes pass,
I'm so glad I have said my prayers.

Louise Black (11)
St Mary's High School, Newry

UNTITLED

B ut it was only supposed to be a bit of fun
    until somebody went and told the nun.
E verybody knew not to tell
    because I had warned them well.
I was the leader see
    when someone told, I said 'It wasn't me!'
N un said 'I was very bold.'
    I will kill whoever told
G angs were meant to stick together
    that's what I thought, but ours - never!

A gainst the rules, they said
    they'll give me work until they think I've paid

B ully was my new name
    I no longer had my fame
U nnecessary as I thought
    I never knew I would get caught
L onely I felt, without my friends
    we planned to stick together till the end
L ousy is how I should feel - said the nun
    but I was only having a bit of fun
Y ou have given this school a bad name.
    How, oh how could I lose my fame?

Louise Doorley (13)
St Mary's High School, Newry

PARENTS

How can we explain them,
Or even understand?
To think that once they were like us,
And now so tall they stand.

Eat your greens,
Wash your teeth,
Tidy that room, or you won't play in the street.
Be in by eight, in bed for nine,
This rhyme we have to listen to time after time.

Corrina McAleavey (12)
St Mary's High School, Newry

MY HAPPIEST DAY

There she lay, far away
In the gleaming sun.
Her dark and light brown coat
Created a lump in my throat.
I knew this magnificent creature was mine!

I walked across the field
To deliver a special meal.
To feed my new pet
When to my amazement
She jumped up and looked down into my eyes.

As I stared back
She moved towards me.
I held out the bucket
She started to eat, she just looked so sweet.
I gave her a pat on the head.

From this moment on
I knew I had a very special pet
My horse - Tara.

Sarah Mackin (13)
St Mary's High School, Newry

START A NEW SCHOOL

It is the beginning of a new year,
I am going into a new school.

I am very nervous,
The school is called St Mary's High School
The girls are all shouting in the hall,
We are going to our first class,
I am very nervous.

It was English,
Our English teacher is called Mrs Morgan,
She is very nice.
It was the end of the class and then we went to science.

Anna McCartney (11)
St Mary's High School, Newry

SCHOOL SOUNDS AND SIGHTS

The creak of a chair, the click of a clock,
As we say our prayers and the lockers lock.
The singing of birds as the sun rises,
We go to tuck and get surprises.

We play about then we go to class,
We go to religion and do our Mass.
We bite our nails and our pen lids,
Then the clock turns three
Now we are:
Free!   Free!   Free!

Christina Flynn (12)
St Mary's High School, Newry

MILLENNIUM

Only 76 days to go
I wonder will everything change?
Will the world come to an end?
Will planes come crashing down?
Will every computer blow up?

If I was in charge of the world
I would change a lot of things.
I would make peace an everyday thing
And murder a thing of the past.

Education would only be for 10 years
And there would be no tests involved
And there would only be three days of school
Instead of the whole five.

Once you've finished school
You could do whatever you want,
Be a model, an actress or teacher
And you wouldn't need the skills.

Money would be a thing of the past
And everything would be five pounds.
Rent and debt and every payment
Would be forgot about.

Although we all know this won't happen
It's nice to think about.
Maybe some things won't come true
But let's all hope peace will!

Carla McSherry (14)
St Mary's High School, Newry

IT'S NOT FAIR!

It's not fair,
It's not my fault,
This bullying has,
To come to a halt.

I should tell,
But it gives me a scare,
Anyway they,
Wouldn't care.

It's not fair,
It's always me.
Why can't they,
Pick on Jamie-Lee?

Patricia Flynn (13)
St Mary's High School, Newry

CHANGING OF SEASONS

As the long summer days draw to an end,
And the long winter nights start to descend.
The leaves are falling from the trees,
And I can even hear a gentle breeze.
Brown, yellow and red as the leaves fall down,
They look like a carpet covering the ground.
The evenings will get darker still,
Thinking of this gives me a chill.
For there's one thing I'll surely miss,
It's the warm, summer evenings and the feeling of bliss.

Lisa Rice (13)
St Mary's High School, Newry

MY GRANNY

My granny is very special to me
I go for walks with her.
She helps me with my homework
And if I'm in trouble and
don't know where to go,
She's always there for me.
I love her so much,
She means so much to me.
If she or I are sick
We're there for one another.
She's proud to be my granny
and I'm proud to be her
granddaughter.

Adele Sarsfield (11)
St Mary's High School, Newry

THE FUTURE

What do you think the world will be like?
Maybe we will all change completely.
Not driving on roads
But flying in the skies above.
Not having to go to school
Get an education at home from a computer.
Not talking on telephones,
Just surfing the net.
I don't know
You tell me!

Debra O'Hagan (13)
St Mary's High School, Newry

GRANNY

Sit by the fire,
Wrapped up nice and warm.
I'll bring you tea,
In this bad storm.
Be glad you're here,
Talking to me.

I'll get you something for your sore knee.
That step was not safe,
When you shut the gate.
I love you to be near,
I feel so safe and have no fear,
You are my granny and I love you so.

But now I have to go,
Tomorrow I'll call for a chat.
Oh I forgot to let in the cat!
So cheerio and take it handy,
You are the world's best granny.

Maria Mathers (11)
St Mary's High School, Newry

WINTER

Winter is a time for fun and play,
Screaming, shouting, playing on the sleigh.
Snow fights, making snowmen, fun and games,
But that's not all, all the trees are bare,
All the animals are rare.
Say goodbye to the sun,
Now the fun has just begun.

Ciara Moley (12)
St Mary's High School, Newry

WHAT IS PEACE?

Peace is a word
That everyone knows
But how do we get it
Or where do we go?
The pain that it eases
Can only be met
When two sides at war
Try to forget.

Throughout the years,
Too much blood has flowed
Heartache and suffering
Is all we are being told.
But why, when the solution
Can be found face to face,
Without bigotry, religion,
Colour or race.

The rewards are that big
That no money can buy,
But only if the leaders
Just sit down and try.
To reach an agreement
To our children we can teach
The most beautiful of words,
Spelt easily - called *peace.*

Orlaigh McKevitt (14)
St Mary's High School, Newry

WHO'S THERE?

Suddenly I woke up
It was very dark.
I couldn't see anything
I was very scared.
Then I heard a noise,
I called out for my mum
But no one answered!
I heard the doors banging
And footsteps coming up the stairs.
They were coming towards my room,
But then my door opened
I didn't see who was there,
I called 'Who's there!'
But there was someone saying
'It's me, it's me!'
I said 'Who are you?'
Suddenly they turned on the light
        It was my brother!

Louise Lennon (13)
St Mary's High School, Newry

STRETCH A LITTLE SMILE

Who invented sadness,
Was it the man above,
Was it someone unlucky,
Maybe unlucky in love?

Who invented sorrow,
Was it someone with no wealth,
Someone who is lonely,
Or someone poor in health?

Whoever this unfortunate character is,
Who invented pain and strife,
Who darkened dreams and hopes,
They didn't see the bright side to life.

They should open their eyes,
And look around for a while,
Lift up their spirits and their heads,
And stretch a little smile.

Karen Fox (14)
St Mary's High School, Newry

BY MYSELF

Waiting, watching by myself,
a victim of a game which I hate to play.
It seems that this game goes on forever,
they call it bullying.

Shouting, laughing, calling names,
sneering at everything I do,
no praise, they only laugh at my pitfalls;
all part of their bullying game.

All because I'm new, wear a brace and glasses,
haven't made friends just yet.
Funny though, it's not my idea of a game.

I call and call, but no one seems to listen.
Unaware that I am in pain
Stuck with that horrible name - bullying.

Waiting, watching by myself.

Kathryn Jennings (13)
St Mary's High School, Newry

SMELLS

I like the smell of freshly cut flowers,
And the smell of petrol coming from cars.

I like the smell of a burning bonfire,
And the smell of smoke raising higher and higher.

I like the smell of cheese and onion crisps,
And the smell of paper-cut snips.

I like the smell of freshly baked buns,
And the smell of fruit coming in tons.

Caroline McKeown (11)
St Mary's High School, Newry

SHOPPING

When I go shopping
with plenty of money
I'm sure to find nothing to buy
Which strikes me as being pretty funny
For when I window-shop
I see all sorts of delights
Yet having no money
This shopping trip's a flop
If my mum comes with me
She finds a lot
Of course her taste is not so hot!

Aisling Starrs (14)
St Mary's High School, Newry

MILLENNIUM

Tick-tock, tick-tock,
Every minute ticking by.
Tick-tock, tick-tock
Every second passing by.

As the countdown starts,
We fill up our glasses,
10, 9, 8, 7
Everyone waiting until the camera flashes.

Party hats, sparklers, fireworks galore,
Everyone waiting to give a big
Roar.

Hip, hip, hooray,
Hip, hip, hooray.
5, 4, 3, 2, 1
Millennium - here we come!

The bells chime - in come the pipers.
It's now official
We're in 2000!

Streamers flying, people crying,
All families together.
It's time for all new adventures.

12 o'clock, it's the 1st January,
A new century just begins.
Everybody full of joy
Will the first born be a boy?

As dawn breaks,
It's time to retire.
Everybody heading for bed.
Will you have a sore head?

Nicola O'Hanlon (13)
St Mary's High School, Newry

OUR NEW SCHOOL

The noise of people in the assembly hall
Prayers being muttered by one and all.
The noise of people going up the stairs;
Walking together, and talking in pairs.
Back to basics with mathematics,
Then to English with grammar.
The sound of teacher's shouting,
And the sound of pupils' laughing.
The sound of the bell ringing,
Like someone screaming in your ear.

The sound of buses starting
The sound of people parting.
All sorts of different sounds,
But the best sound has to be the last bell.
Even though it screams in your ear,
It means the end of school!

Treise Lively (11)
St Mary's High School, Newry

NIGHT-TIME

When the day turns into night
The sky above is lovely and bright
The sun goes away and the moon comes out
The streets are quiet with no one about.

We all lie sleeping in our beds
Peace and harmony surrounding our heads
It's time for us to relax and pray
To thank God for the wonderful day.

If we wake up during the night
And see something strange we get a fright
Shadows up against the wall
Noises coming from the hall.

When we wake up in the morning
The streets are packed with children running
Off to school away they go
It will be night-time again before they know.

Claire Loughran (14)
St Mary's High School, Newry

LONELY

I am sick of being bullied
by people I know, every
minute, wherever I go.
Sometimes I wish I really
was dead, those people
are driving me crazy
they're wrecking my head.

I may not be perfect
I may not look right
just give me one chance
and you'll see that I'm nice.
I am in need of just one
friend because I don't
want to be alone from
now to the end.

Rachel O'Callaghan (12)
St Mary's High School, Newry

WHY?

Why does someone close to you have to die?
If anyone can answer this, please tell me why!
I can't understand if someone you have loved,
Has their life taken away and is sent up above.

Why does violence occur?
We sit and think *I'm glad I'm not there!*
Looking at our TV screens seeing people in tears,
Knowing that our tiny problems are nothing compared to their fears.

Why does bullying take place?
Personally I feel that this is a total disgrace.
People are being picked on and being laughed at,
Some are called names like *skinny* or *fat*.

Why do people drink and drive?
Knowing that there is a chance they could take away a life.
It is an irresponsible and foolish thing to do,
Who would think of doing this - me or you?

Why do people smoke when they are young?
Do they think it is a bit of fun?
They know they will damage their health,
And it certainly is not doing anything for their wealth.

Unsolved are all of these things!
But look at the heartache that each one brings.
A lot of questions are floating around
But the big question is, will the answer to them ever be found?

Sarah Maguire (14)
St Mary's High School, Newry

PARENTS' SAYINGS

Don't they understand I have
a social life?
Places to go, people to see.
Why won't they stop putting
pressure on me!

Eat up your dinner and you will
be strong.
Don't you know the difference
between right and wrong?

Don't go out with him.
Don't you be running around with her.
All they do is nag, it's just
not fair.

Do the dishes, tidy up this place.
Get that make-up off your face.
You're still too young to go out
at nights.
Don't you be getting into any fights.

Get a bad report at school then
you're grounded for a year.
Get home from school that day
and they grab you by the ear.

Make me proud, make sure you behave.
One of the many pieces of advice my
parents gave.

On the other hand, they buy me new
clothes and take me places.
But most of all I know they love me
by the smile on their faces.

Jill Murphy (14)
St Mary's High School, Newry

AUTUMN

1, 2, 3 as I count more leaves
They swirl off the tree,
Falling to the wet ground.
Autumn comes so quick,
Spring seems like years ago
Winter seems to be very near.

The young children try to
Catch the falling leaves.
The dark nights bring frost
And the early mornings look cold.
We wear our tracksuits
No more short skirts!

I wish that it was summer again!

Karen Redmond (12)
St Mary's High School, Newry

SHOPPING POEM

Christmas shopping is the best
It's where your patience is put to the test.
Standing in queues a mile long
You're only slightly moving along.

Shopping for toys it's like a maze
Trying to get your child the latest craze.
Power Rangers and Barbies galore
You always forget what you came in for.

Children don't want little board games
They want computer games.
Look at the price that can't be right!
I guess I have to pay, but it gave me a fright.

So hurry up and head for the sales
And when all else fails.
You could buy your presents early
And save yourself a wasted journey.

Linda Mullard (14)
St Mary's High School, Newry

MEMORIES

One memory I can remember well
Is when I stood on the wall and fell.
My dad put me back on my feet,
And said I could have some sweets.
I wanted more than a milky way
But Dad only had 15p to pay.
At this time I was only three,
And I was wearing dungarees.
Really, I didn't mean to steal,
But in my pocket I put fruit pastilles.
My dad saw what I had done,
And said ' I didn't pay for that one!'
I took the sweets back into the shop,
And told the shop owner my stealing would stop.

Deirbhle O'Brien (11)
St Mary's High School, Newry

WINTER IS . . .

Stars crackling in the sky
Twinkling, bright and bold
In the dark night, sky blue
And the moon so cold.

The snow begins to fall
A thick white blanket covering the ground
Too deep to walk, it's soft and cuddly
Like fluffy clouds floating in the air.

The animals are hibernating
All asleep, so quiet and peaceful
Warm and snug all wrapped
In a ball.

The cold gets to me
It makes me sneeze.
I can't wait till spring
Comes again.

Ellen Rice (12)
St Mary's High School, Newry

SMELLS

Smelly socks and smelly shoes
Bad smells like out of date food.
Rotten fish and chimney smoke
Rotten eggs it makes me choke.

I love the smell of the season of spring
The sweet scent of flowers it's a beautiful thing.
The nice perfume which I spray
These are the smells of every day.

Nicola Lowry (12)
St Mary's High School, Newry

I Am

I am the wind that blows in your face
I am the fire that keeps you warm
I am the moon that shines in the night
I am the sun that makes things grow
I am a hawk upon a cliff
I am a flower that blooms in the day
I am an owl that hunts at night.

I am a fish within a pool
I am a fluffy white cloud that floats by
I am a wave returning home
I am a child that makes people happy
I am a hill where poets climb
I am a mind of happy thoughts
I am.

Sinead McArdle (12)
St Mary's High School, Newry

The Victim

T   he tension in every moment
H   urt and frightened
E   mptiness inside

V   ery
I   ntelligent but ostracised
C   ompared with everyone else
T   troubled and
I   solated
M   ind filled with fear and despair.

Nicola Connolly (12)
St Mary's High School, Newry

DEAR DAD

Today I dream, more a memory than sleep.
I dream of you, the only man to make my tears
last so long.

They never seem to fall, yet they touch
everything I do, everyone but you.
Why? Well, you never were a reality to me,
never a dream, more my nightmare,
one that just won't leave.

You made them all cry, all of us never explaining
why! Why? To you love is nothing.
Family also nothing.
Well sometimes I see you from the memories,
I look a lot like you
and you don't even know me!
That makes me sad,
but my memories, they can't scare me.
So I'll sleep now.

Rochelle Davren (13)
St Mary's High School, Newry

MY BROTHER

He hits, he kicks
He throws his fists
He fights with other boys
If he wins he runs in to hide.
And if he doesn't he runs in to cry
The only time I see him at peace
Is when he is fast asleep.

Sarah Harte (12)
St Mary's High School, Newry

MY NEW SCHOOL

The yawning of the people in the hall
And prayers being said by one and all.
After assembly it's like a stampede of
Elephants going up the stairs.
In form class, time to relax, get the
Register out and on to the next class.

PE's first and after, the netball match
Their cheering and jeering like a pack
Of chimps.

Now it's technology, where you hear that
Buzzing noise of the machines and it's
Like a million bees crowding around
A beehive.

Library now, and everyone's as quiet as
Mice reading their books and enjoying
Them too.

Oh yes, it's lunchtime, the smell of that
Food really puts you in the mood and
The shouting of the girls sound like
A gaggle of geese.

A couple of more classes and then that
Screaming bell goes and the girls race down
The stairs, out the door and then it's -
Silence!

Keeva Murtagh (11)
St Mary's High School, Newry

OSTRACISED

What do you see in me?
What do you see?
What are you thinking when you look at me?
You don't seem to like me, even though
I am nice.
I am the same as you with
Many talents of my own.
Why do you always leave me
Standing alone?

I pretend I don't hear
I pretend I don't see.
Standing alone, almost in tears
I wish you could feel all of my fears.
Why don't you accept me
like you do with the others?
Is it because I am not very pretty,
wear glasses and have a brace?
But I wish you could see beyond
into me.

I would love to be your friend
Some day I may!
So open your heart open and see
not a helpless weak girl.
Look closer - see me!

Emma Crawley (13)
St Mary's High School, Newry

HALLOWE'EN

Hallowe'en is a day
With spooks and goons.
Witches, vampires and ghosts.
Hallowe'en parties with sweets and treats.

You and your friends might go around scaring people.
You might even go trick or treating.
Other people might even try and scare you.
But you can't be quite sure if they are real or not

So beware!
You might be in for a scare.

Tanya Payne (12)
St Mary's High School, Newry

DARK

I hate it when it comes,
it scares me half to death,
I always call for Mum and Dad
and run out of breath.
I know about the monsters
that come out at night
and give you such a fright.
Mum says there's no need to be afraid
but I don't know what to do
as she scares me too!

Laura McGrath (14)
St Michael's Grammar School, Lurgan

Toys

Toys, toys everywhere
On the landing, on the stair.
Toys, toys all around,
Piled up high, on the ground.
Toys, toys so many toys,
Some for girls and some for boys.
Toys, toys big and small,
Dolls and teddies you can have them all.
Toys, toys are so much fun,
Play in the rain or out in the sun.
Toys, toys all different kinds,
For different children with different minds.
Toys, toys give your friends a go,
With Tinky-Winky, Dipsy, La-La and Po.
Toys, toys pick what you like,
A big red train or a bright shiny bike.
Toys, toys play with your friend,
You will never want the fun to end.

Alina Breen (9)
St Michael's Grammar School, Lurgan

Hallowe'en Night

One cold and windy Hallowe'en Night,
A witch and a wizard began to fight.
The wizard had a sword, the witch a broom
And it seemed that one would reach their doom.

The duel continued throughout the night
And passers by got such a fright.
When the wizard began to use his magic
It seemed as though the end would be tragic.

They fought and they fought with powerful force
And not the witch or the wizard showed any remorse.
Their spells were colliding in a dangerous way
So the pair decided to call it a day.

There emerged no winner that Hallowe'en Night
But every year since, they continued their fight.
So lock your doors during this season
From reading this poem you should know the reason.

Kerry-Anne Cushley (17)
St Michael's Grammar School, Lurgan

THE CIRCUS

Today was the day; it had finally come,
The streets were full of wonder and fun.
There were elephants, lion, monkeys and clowns,
Yes, it was true the circus had come to town.

Far in the distance the tent could be seen,
With strong vivid colours of red, blue and green.
The music, the laughter, the cheerful smiles,
Of tiny little children who had come from miles and miles.

The show was fantastic there was no doubt about that,
There was music, fun, laughter and chat.
The wonder and amazement as the fireworks started,
Suggested that the circus had eventually parted.

I'll never forget the magnificent day,
When the great big circus came our way.
I was sorry to see it disappear,
And, I hope that it will be back again next year.

Louise Mulholland
St Michael's Grammar School, Lurgan

I LOVE TO DREAM

I had a dream last night.
I love to dream!
I dreamt of far off places and washing machines.
I flew to Greece and I got all slippy and slimy
I flew to Venice (that was a menace)
I love to dream!

I've been to Mars and on the moon.
I got there in my little wooden spoon.
Then we ate all the Milky Way
After all that I was really full.
I love to dream!

I met a spaceman and some talking books
When I brought them home I got some funny looks.
We swam through some lakes all made of fizzy pop
I love to dream!

We ate all the jelly in Jello Mountain
Then we danced in the biggest fountain
Lots of chocolate and ice-cream
Oh no it was all a dream!

Christina McQuillan
St Michael's Grammar School, Lurgan

WITCHES - READ ON . . .

The Hallowe'en dance will be soon
When the sun will then pass round the moon.
Kids are so excited
Dying to be invited
Hope the music's going to be out of tune.

The Cauldron School Of Witches is the venue
Where anything goes on the menu
From ice-cream with lice
To eyeballs with rice
And a slimy strange creature called Zanue.

So witches go polish that broom
For the time is beginning to loom
When spells will be taught
Great warriors fought
And that night's filled with darkness and gloom.

Invitations to the Devil School Of Horns
Where replies must be sent back by morn
Hurry up, don't delay
Make your mind up today
Or you'll wish that you hadn't been born!

Lisa Mincher
St Michael's Grammar School, Lurgan

THE UNWANTED GUEST

At last I'm not a baby,
The moment, it has finally come,
The smile is now upon my face,
I no longer feel so glum.

I twisted and I turned it,
But alas it would not budge,
It seemed so determined to stay there,
For how long I could not judge.

My friends, they loved to tease me,
They could not understand,
How much it would just please me,
To have it in my hand.

At five o'clock this evening,
One tug and out it came,
That tooth has finally gone to rest,
I say this without shame.

Siobhan Murphy (16)
St Michael's Grammar School, Lurgan

BRUSSEL SPROUTS

Mum and Dad tell me they'll make me big and strong,
But I think they've got it all wrong.
They are green and taste really bad,
When I see them I get mad.

My mum says they taste alright
But I don't see her eat them every night.
If I had one wish
Brussel sprouts would be dismissed.

When I taste them I feel sick
My head goes dizzy
And my parents take the mick.

Ciaran Magee
St Michael's Grammar School, Lurgan

GREENS

Broccoli, cabbage, parsnips and peas
Don't make me eat them they weaken my knees.
Greens can't be good for you I don't care what they say
I won't eat them - I won't - if I've to starve every day.

I had a dream that they came alive
two heads, four arms and six hundred eyes.
They chased me through parks, hedges and wood
I tried to hide from them but that was no good.

They shoot at me with rifles, swords, knives and guns
I said when I eat them they give me the runs.
The leader was worst, he called out my name
When I didn't answer the rest did the same.

When I woke I was screaming, Mum rushed to my bed,
'What's wrong with you darling?' - 'Killers,' I said.
She told me to calm down - they weren't really mean
I said that forever I won't eat a green.

Weekly for dinner Mum made me chips
Twenty years later I grew at the hips.
Advice I will give you remembering that day
Eat greens or bad dreams just won't go away.

Natalie Kerr & Roísín Austin
St Michael's Grammar School, Lurgan

THE TOOTH FAIRIES

They come out at night
When the sun's out of sight
Some say they're pink,
Some say they're white.

They've got loads of money
And that's the truth
And they'll give you a coin
In exchange for your tooth.

So in the morning when you arise,
Look under your pillow with your sleepy eyes,
And you'll find that the fairies have left a surprise.

And so little children with gaps in your teeth,
Don't spend all your money on rotten old sweets
And listen very carefully when your mum and dad say,
Brush them lovely teeth at least twice a day.

Katie Doran
St Michael's Grammar School, Lurgan

MEDICINE

When it pours out of the jar,
It's like runny tar.
It comes in yellow, pink and red,
And when you drink it, it goes to your head.

It's like drinking coloured blood,
But I'd rather eat mud.
It's revolting and gooey,
And certainly not chewy.

You get it in the chemist shop
And all you have to do is drink one drop.
It's meant to make you better,
Or that's what it says on the prescription letter.

As they say, it does really cure you,
Whether or not you have a cough or the flu.

Colin Carbery (15)
St Michael's Grammar School, Lurgan

IMAGINARY FRIEND

My niece she has an imaginary friend.
She found him under the stairs.
It was a mouse in the house under the stairs,
And she decided to call it Fred.

Every day she'd pretend to feed him,
Sneaking cheese under the stairs,
But it never was eaten,
It was just an imaginary friend.

She put under-blankets and pillows for him to sleep.
She loved her dear old Fred,
Taking good care of him under the stairs,
But he was only an imaginary friend.

And now time has passed,
And she has forgotten that mouse
That once hid below the stairs,
But all the same it was only an imaginary mouse.

Peter Haddock
St Michael's Grammar School, Lurgan

THUNDER AND LIGHTNING

The sky gives a flash
And the rain starts to lash.
Then there is a clap of thunder
When will it be over, I wonder?

People are afraid of thunder and lightning.
The flash and noise is so frightening.
After the rain begins to stop.
But then come in heavier drops.

The lights begin to flicker,
People get a wee bit sicker.
The rain gets as heavy as it was before
People think to themselves, there's got to be more.

The lightning then strikes the ground
It makes a very loud sound.
People scream and start to run
They wish they had the sun.

Suddenly the sun comes to display,
Maybe it's going to be a brilliant day.
The people are happy and glad
Now the heavens aren't so mad!

John Haughey
St Michael's Grammar School, Lurgan

UNTITLED

When I was young I had a lot of fun
I thought I was a cowboy shooting my gun,
but at the end of the day my mum would say,
'Come on Jimmy, no more play.'

I would cry and yap
and ask to stay
but Mum always said
there was no way.

So we would go home
and I would be in a huff
but then I'd settle down
and watch TV and stuff.

I would go to bed
and get a good rest
because tomorrow
I was going to make it the best.

I would wake up in the morning
as bright as the sun
and get myself ready
to have some fun.

At the end of the day,
I dread when Mum says,
'Come on Jimmy, no more play.'

Keith Totton
St Michael's Grammar School, Lurgan

THE TEENY TINY BUG

There was a teeny tiny bug,
On a teeny tiny leaf,
And he munched and he crunched,
With his teeny tiny teeth.

He chomped and he chewed,
He swallowed and he slurped,
Then all of a sudden,
He did a *big* burp!

The burp roared out like thunder,
And the leaf began to shake,
Then from underneath his tiny legs,
The little leaf did break.

He tumbled down towards the ground,
At a million miles per hour,
But he landed on his teeny butt,
And so he was unharmed.

The little bug was starving
He could see no leaves to eat,
Little did he know,
That he was in for such a treat!

Because very soon came autumn,
And the leaves began to fall,
And as they did, the little bug,
Bet he could eat them all!

Caroline McNally
St Michael's Grammar School, Lurgan

THE MONSTER IN MY MIND

Deep in Mark's closet under some clothes,
Lives a very large monster with a very long nose,
He has twenty fingers and thirty toes,
But what he eats no one really knows.

Mark had thought of the obvious things,
Like spiders, snakes, small bats' wings,
Or horses, goats and a bull with a ring,
Maybe even wasps that sting.

Then he thought a little harder,
And his mind wandered to the kitchen larder,
What in there would a monster eat?
Crisps, fruit maybe something sweet.

Then he looked around and thought again,
In his mind now the answer was plain,
The answer really wasn't that wild,
What the monster wanted was a human child.

Mark pulled up his blankets and snuggled down deep,
And slowly but surely he drifted to sleep.
Then in the middle of the night he awoke with a fright,
And jumped up quickly to turn on the light.

He gazed at the closet and went over to see,
Under the clothes where the monster would be,
He flung back the clothes and what did he find
Nothing at all it was all in the mind.

Deep in Mark's closet under some clothes,
There was no monster with a very long nose,
All that was there to see,
Were the clothes Mark's mum had laid out for PE.

Niall Moore
St Michael's Grammar School, Lurgan

LOVELY PUDDING

Pudding, pudding I love pudding,
I eat it for my tea,
I'd rather, rather eat it,
Than a carrot or a pea.

I hear it's bad for your teeth,
I believe it's very good,
I really, really love it,
It's my very favourite food.

It comes in different flavours,
It comes in different pots,
I love Yorkshire pudding,
It really is tops.

It's lovely with pork pie,
It's lovely with beans.
It's lovely when it's chocolate,
It's the nicest I've ever seen.

Lovely, lovely custard,
When it's poured over the top,
How I'd love some lovely pudding
All cooked and hot.

Conor McAlinden
St Michael's Grammar School, Lurgan

MY NEW SCHOOL

In the assembly hall we gathered,
Rows of jet-black blazers,
Striped ties all knotted well,
Shoes polished brightly,
This army was prepared.

We were led away in ranks,
So far the day was good,
Timetables were well studied,
Bell rings,
Signalling food.

After lunch we worked hard,
Our teachers seemed okay,
Our first day was nearly at an end,
The new rules were complicated,
But I knew they would come in time.

As the last bell rang,
And we headed for home,
I talked to my friends,
Looked back at the school,
And realised it was mine.

Kieran McConaghy (11)
St Paul's Junior High School, Lurgan

THE BULLY

A bully tells you what to do
and makes you do what you don't want to.
He's cruel and mean
and steals jelly beans.
He beats you up and causes you pain
over and over again.
He'll flush your head down the loo
He'll shake you until you're blue.
He'll steal your money,
And think he's funny.
A bully is a poor little child,
who's frightened inside.
A bully is a bully
but when it comes to fighting he's a coward.

Kevin Barry Lennon
St Paul's Junior High School, Lurgan

MY NEW SCHOOL

As I entered my new school,
A thought came to my head,
What if everyone thought I was a fool?
Oh I wished I'd stayed in bed!

What if all the teachers were mean
And all the pupils were rough?
They all seem so very keen,
When I was thinking this was tough.

Then I saw my friend,
And all my fears disappeared.
He said he was hoping this day would end,
Then our form teacher suddenly appeared.

She brought us to our new class and introduced us,
She told us this is our new beginning and not the end,
Now I see there was no need to fuss,
This school will be a happy place for me and my friend.

Tony McConville (12)
St Paul's Junior High School, Lurgan

SHIP OF DREAMS

The green hills of Ireland slowly disappear from view,
As we steamed into the western sunset and history,
A dream of a man named Andrews,
A new decade,
The world's most famous liner carried to the bottom,
A treasure trove of secrets,
A ship drowned by luxury,
First class all the way,
Everything about the ship was a nightmarish scale,
A ship banished into the mystical waters of the icy
                                        Atlantic Ocean
We will bless the lives lost that night and the
                                lives forever altered.
A ship of dreams.
RMS Titanic.

Conor Mallon (11)
St Paul's Junior High School, Lurgan

MY NEW SCHOOL

My first day was great I could hardly wait.
Nothing went wrong, as sweet as a song.
I gave a jerk I gave a jump,
in my throat there was no lump.
I got dressed like lightning flashing,
there was no doubt this day would be smashing.

Teachers, teachers everywhere
only one gave me a scare.
The sound of shouting blasted my ears,
then the bell rang to boost my fears.
There were boys and more boys short and stout
Everyone walking not running about.
We took a left, then a right,
everyone started to fill with fright.

A new beginning would almost start,
after form we had some art.
All the nerves had finally settled,
and after a time the lunch bell rattled.
The food was nice, I had curry and rice.
It filled me up right to the top,
and when I was finished I had to stop.

After lunch we had PE, then some maths 1, 2, 3
Back on the road heading for Hell,
we had some French with Mrs Bell.
Back to form for some RE
Mrs Johnson we were glad to see.
Thirty-five minutes had gone so slow,
roll on tomorrow for another go.

Christopher McCann (11)
St Paul's Junior High School, Lurgan

HALLOWE'EN

Let the awful news be spread,
Hallowe'en's the eve of the dead,
It's time for witches, ghouls and ghosts,
Keep away from any hosts.

Vampires and demons who drink your blood,
To kill them you need a piece of wood,
Sharpen it, point it, make it good,
Get some garlic, (that's a food).

Witches always cast their spells,
Take a piece of salt and lead, that witch is
                              gonna go to Hell.
Steal a spell book from a witch,
Make her bound, make her itch,
Get her dead that mean old witch.

Now you know to watch your back,
Make sure you also watch your neck.
Let the awful news be spread,
Hallowe'en's here, it's the eve of the dead.

Damien McIlduff (12)
St Paul's Junior High School, Lurgan

BARN OWL - (FATHER'S STORY)

Asleep, in my bedroom lying
woken by a shot.
I was unsure of what was
there in the family barn.
The sun shone brightly.
I gathered my clothes,
rushed down those steep stairs
to see the gun beside my son.
I feared the worst.
At the end of the barn,
lying on damp straw,
what can only be described as a thing.
Deformed by a piercing bullet,
struggling for its life.
So I picked up the gun,
gave it to my son.
He ended what he begun.

Shane Coleman (14)
St Paul's Junior High School, Lurgan